HOW TO BUILD A
POWER HACKSAW WITH VISE

Written and Illustrated by
VINCENT R. GINGERY

Printed in U. S. A.

First Printing 1992
Revised Edition 2000

Library Of Congress
Catalog Card Number 92-90772

International Standard
Book Number 1-878087-12-6

Published By
David J. Gingery Publishing LLC
P.O. Box 318
Rogersville, MO 65742

TABLE OF CONTENTS

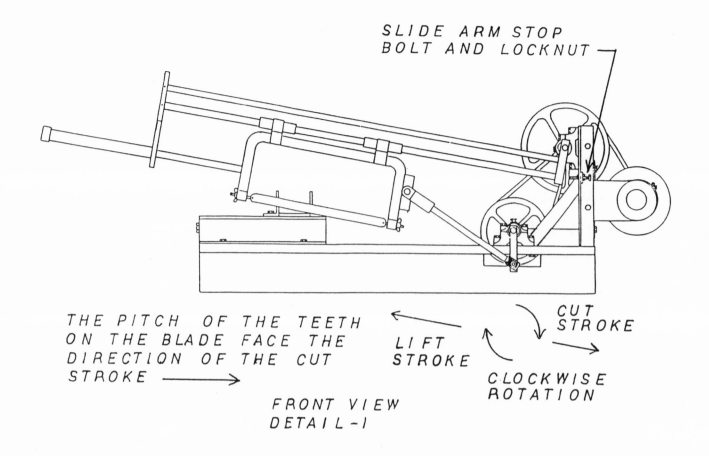

SLIDE ARM STOP
BOLT AND LOCKNUT

THE PITCH OF THE TEETH
ON THE BLADE FACE THE
DIRECTION OF THE CUT
STROKE ———————>

LIFT
STROKE

CUT
STROKE

CLOCKWISE
ROTATION

FRONT VIEW
DETAIL-1

INTRODUCTION

The hacksaw machine described in this manual is simply a power driven hacksaw frame. This particular machine uses a crank and connecting rod driven by an electric motor to operate the hacksaw frame.

The cutting is done on the return stroke. As the crank moves in a downward direction it has a tendency to pull the saw blade down against the work. As the crank moves in an upward direction it pushes the saw up and away from the work, allowing for smooth and simple operation. The saw pictured in detail 1 on page 4 has just finished the cutting stroke and is beginning the lift stroke.

The saw presented in this manual is light and weighs just a little over 50 pounds. Often times I need to cut material that is 20 feet long. In the past it had not only been a problem cutting this material by hand, but it had also been a problem of trying to fit this material in the garage and prop it up with saw horses in order to cut it . Now all I have to do is set my portable hacksaw outside the garage door, clamp the material that I want to cut in the vise, and let the saw do its work. Of course, with shorter and easier to handle material, I am able to set the saw on the work bench and let it do its work there.

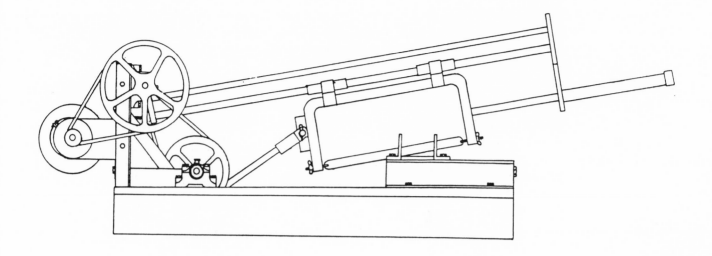

REAR VIEW
DETAIL-2

I designed the saw to travel at 60 strokes per minute. After trying several different speeds I found that the saw did its best work at this speed and still remained easy to control. Using a good quality 14 teeth per inch flexible saw blade the saw will cut straight through a piece of 1/4" x 3" flat bar in just a couple of minutes.

Another advantage to owning a power hacksaw is that the saw blades cost a lot less than band saw blades. For instance, you can by a good quality hacksaw blade for $1.00 to a $1.50. A bandsaw replacement blade starts at $6.00 and the price goes up from there. The saw blade that I tend to use the most for cutting mild steel is a good quality, high speed, flexible, bi-metal blade, with 14 teeth per inch. If you're not careful the flexible blades will twist slightly when they begin the cut. This will cause the saw to cut crooked. The risk of this can be reduced if you are careful when you begin the cut and don't let the saw bear down to hard on the work. "All hard" blades are available, and tend to cut more accurately, although they break easily. So you still have to use caution no matter which blade you use when you begin your cut. Instead of twisting slightly these "all hard" blades will break. In choosing a saw blade the general rule is that 3 teeth should be in contact with the work. So thin work requires more teeth per inch.

Most hardware stores carry 18, 24 and 32 T.P.I. hand hacksaw blades. I purchased the 14 tooth per inch blade at a local industrial supply company. The "all hard" blades commonly used on power hacksaw machines were not easy for me to find in my local area. A good place to buy "all hard" blades at a reasonable price is the Enco Manufacturing Company. Their toll free nationwide phone number at the time of this publication was, 1-800-621-4145.

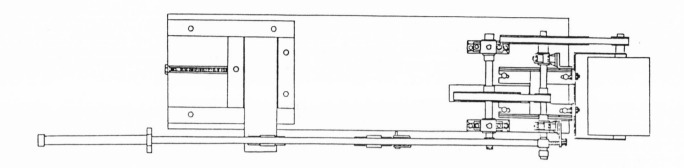

When I built this saw I included a weight arm in the design. My purpose in this was not only to hold weights in place if they were needed, but to also add support to the saw frame slide arm structure. I have experimented with weights added to the weight arm, to see if I could improve the performance of the saw, and have found that with this particular design weights seem to be unnecessary. At 60 strokes per minute the saw runs very smooth and the saw frame stays under control. If you beefed up the design of the saw using heavier material, a motor with a larger horsepower rating and ran the saw at 90 strokes per minute, weights would be necessary for sure to keep the saw frame under control and the saw blade against the work. These weights could be made by drilling a hole, the same diameter as the weight arm, in short sections of 3" round rod or 3" square stock. These weights could then be slipped on the weight arm and held in place with shaft collars.

The power hacksaw is made up of several sub-assemblies. These are the base, countershaft stand, countershaft, crankshaft, vise, saw frame, saw frame slide assembly and the connecting rod assembly. Detail 4 on page 7 shows the different parts of the saw. All of the movable parts of the saw have bronze sleeve bearings.

The base is built with 2x4 lumber and 3/4" plywood. It is assembled with nails and glue.

The countershaft stand is a simple assembly built from 1 1/4" x 1/8" angle iron. It is the heart of the entire project. The motor mount is bolted to the stand. The countershaft assembly is also bolted to the stand.

An arc welder capable of at least 100 amps is needed to assemble this stand, as well as some of the other components of the saw. If you do not own a welder do not let that stop you from doing this project. They can be rented for a lot less than you might think. Maybe a friend will let you borrow his, or maybe you can find a bargain on a used one.

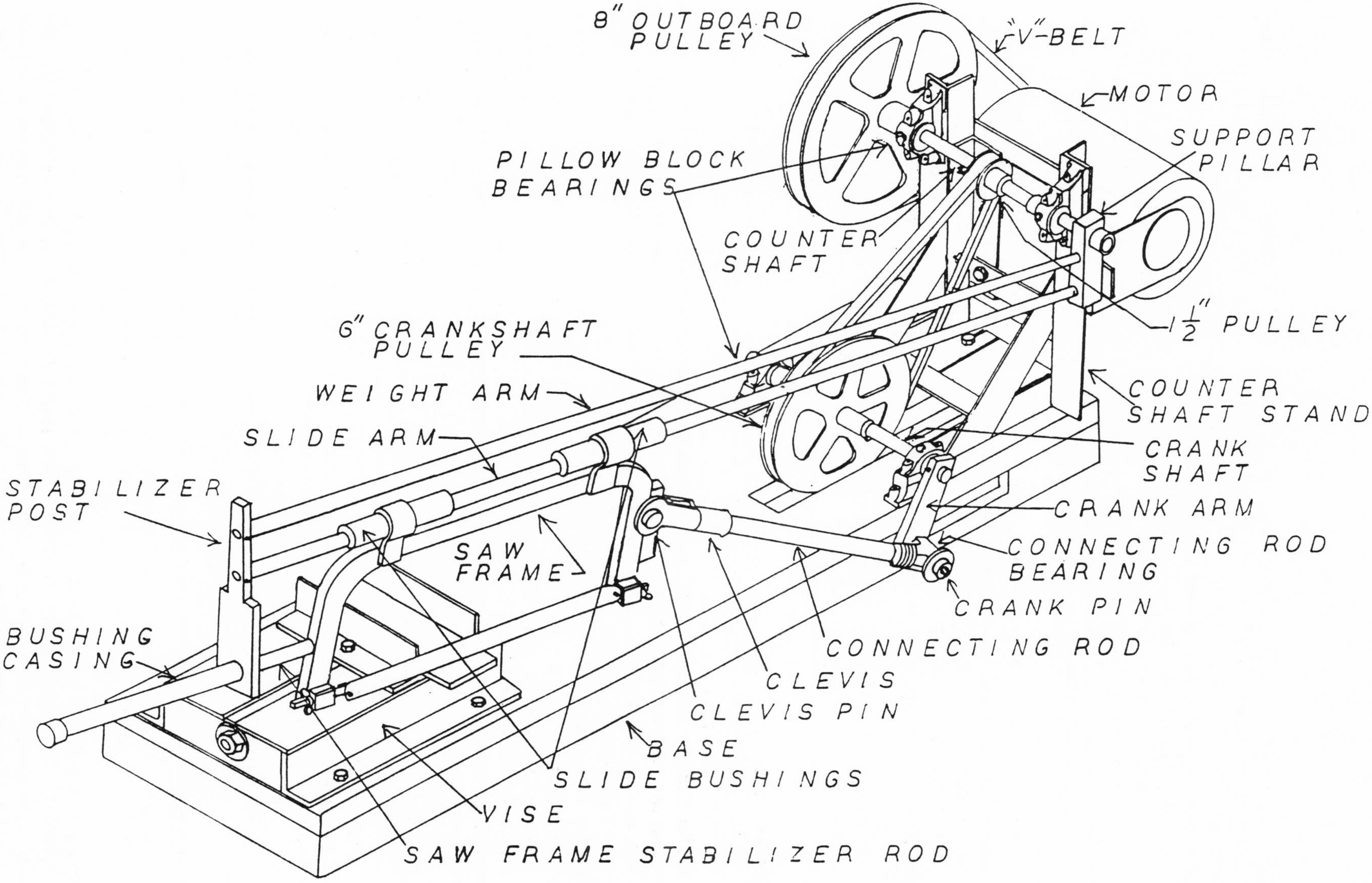

8" OUTBOARD PULLEY

"V"-BELT

MOTOR

SUPPORT PILLAR

1½" PULLEY

COUNTER SHAFT STAND

CRANK SHAFT

CRANK ARM

CONNECTING ROD

CONNECTING ROD BEARING

CRANK PIN

CONNECTING ROD

PILLOW BLOCK BEARINGS

COUNTER SHAFT

6" CRANKSHAFT PULLEY

WEIGHT ARM

SLIDE ARM

CLEVIS

CLEVIS PIN

BASE

SLIDE BUSHINGS

VISE

SAW FRAME STABILIZER ROD

SAW FRAME

STABILIZER POST

BUSHING CASING

DETAIL-4

7

The motor I used is a 1/3 H.P. and runs at 1750 R.P.M.. It has a 1/2" shaft and a 1 1/2" pulley is placed on the shaft. Chances are you will have an old motor laying around. I would say that any 115 volt electric motor rated at a 1/4 horse or better would do. The R.P.M. rating is not that critical because the speed of the saw can be adjusted by using different size reduction pulleys. If you don't have a motor, be sure to check around at second hand stores, garage and rummage sales etc.. I have seen, and in fact have bought these types of motors for as little as fifty cents. It really pays to shop around, not only for motors, but for all your other materials as well.

The 1/2" countershaft is supported by two pillow block bearings that are bolted to the countershaft stand. Power is transferred to the 8" outboard pulley mounted on the countershaft from the 1 1/2" pulley mounted on the motor shaft. The speed of the countershaft has been reduced by these pulleys to 278 R.P.M.. The saw frame support pillar is also placed on the end of the countershaft.

The 1/2" crankshaft is supported by two pillow block bearings that are bolted to the base. Power is transferred to the 6" crankshaft pulley by a 1 1/2" pulley mounted on the center of the countershaft. The speed of the crankshaft has been reduced to 61 R.P.M. by these two pulleys. The 4" crank arm is attached to the end of the crankshaft.

The connecting rod is a 9 1/2" long piece of 1/2" round rod threaded 1/2 - 20 on both ends. One end screws into the crank arm bearing which is a modified 3/8" brass union tee. The crank arm bearing is attached to the crank arm by a 1/2" x 1 1/2" shoulder bolt refered to as the crank pin. The other end of the connecting rod screws into the saw frame clevis. The clevis is attached to the saw frame by a 1/2" x 1 1/2" clevis pin.

The saw frame is formed from 3/4" x 3/8" flat bar. The saw blade is attached to the saw frame by two tension bolts. These bolts are made from 1/4" key stock. One end is threaded 1/4-20 and the other end has a piece of 1/8" round rod brazed to it. This round rod is what the saw blade hooks to. These are referred to as blade pins. The blade pins need to be strong and not brittle. I used a piece of an 8 penny nail for the blade pins in my saw.

The saw frame slide bushing assembly consists of two pieces of 1/2" black pipe 3 3/4" long. A 1/2" x 5/8" bushing is pressed into both ends of each pipe. Each bushed section of pipe is attached to the saw frame by a simple hanger bracket made from 1" x 1/8" strap. The saw frame with bushing assembly attached slides onto the 1/2" round rod referred to as the slide arm. The slide arm screws into the slide and weight arm support pillar located on the countershaft. Another piece of 1/2" round rod, referred to as the weight arm, also screws into the support pillar.

A stabilizer post made from 3/8" x 2" flat bar is attached to the other end of the slide and weight arm. It is secured with set screws. A 10" length of 1/2" black pipe, with a 1/2" x 5/8" bushing pressed into one end, is welded to the stabilizer post. This is referred to as the bushing casing. A 10" length of 1/2" round rod, referred to as the saw frame stabilizer rod, is welded to the saw frame. It travels back and forth inside the bushing casing as the saw frame moves. This serves to stabilize the saw frame. It also allows us to adjust the saw frame by loosening the set screws in the stabilizer post and moving the saw frame, either left or right, until it is square with the work.

The vise is built entirely of 1/4" thick material and is operated by a standard 1/2" ratchet and a 3/4" socket. The jaws open 6 1/2", and are 7" wide and 2" deep. The material used, as well as the size of the vise, can be scaled up or down depending on your needs.

I have included a list of most of the tools that I used in this project. Nothing exotic is required and most are found in the average shop. One thing that does deserve mention here are the larger size drill bits used in the project. They consist of assorted sizes up to 7/8" and they all have a 1/2" cut down shank. You need to be careful when drilling with drill bits this large, particularly if you are using a 1/2" hand drill. Those things can hang up and throw you half way across the shop. Also, keep any loose clothing and long hair out of the way when you are drilling. If your shop is not equipped with drill bits this large maybe you can rely on that good friend again and borrow a set. If you plan on buying the necessary drill bits for this project be sure and shop around. I bought a complete set of drill bits sizes 17/32" through 1" from K.I.T. Tools for the same price as one drill bit at the local hardware store. These are not the best quality drill bits, but they work fine as long as I take my time and step drill all my holes. If you plan on using your large size drill bits on a regular basis you may be able to justify spending more money and getting a better set. If you want a catalog from K.I.T. Tools their toll free number at the time of this publication was, 1-800-521-6579.

All holes must be drilled and tapped straight. If you have a drill press it will make things easier. If you don't, it takes just a little care and a conscious effort and you can drill straight. A small machinist square is helpful to check straightness of the drill. Proceed with caution as you tap these holes and make sure the taps go into the holes straight. Use plenty of cutting oil and back the tap off every turn or so to clear the threads. It pays to take your time. Their is nothing more aggravating than to have a part almost complete and break a tap off.

Remember take your time and be accurate in your work because this will determine how straight your saw cuts when it is complete. If you mount the countershaft stand to the base crooked, the saw will cut crooked. If you drill the hole in the crankshaft bearing crooked, the saw frame will wobble from side to side and make handling the saw difficult as well as causing it to cut crooked. These are only a couple of examples. Each part is dependent on the other, so each step should be carried out carefully.

The most important thing in this project, as well as any project, is safety. There are many hazards involved and no effort has been made to point out all of them. The author of this manual is not an engineer and no engineering has been applied to this project. The design for this hacksaw is a combination of ideas seen on other hacksaw machines and the plans to build them. Each detail presented in this manual is subject to your own appraisal and you are fully responsible for your own safety and that of any others who may be injured due to your pursuit of this activity. Remember you are building a power hacksaw that cuts metal. If it can cut metal it can certainly cut you as well. When welding, be sure to wear an approved welding hood. Make sure their are no flammable liquids close to the work area. The area should be clean and the floor swept. Remove any rags or other flammable material from the welding area. The room should be well ventilated so as to remove the harmful vapors that are caused from welding. People in the room with you should be instructed not to look at the harmful rays caused by the welding arc. Be sure and wear eye protection at all times when involved in any shop activities. Think through each move and ask yourself if their is anything involved that can hurt either yourself, or an innocent bystander and proceed with caution. It only takes a second to be safe and it could save you, or someone close to you, from a life of unhappiness. If you're ready let's build a power hacksaw.

MATERIAL LIST

1- piece of 3/4" plywood 36" x 10" (base top)

1- 8' 2x4 (base frame)

8- #8D nails (assemble base frame)

14- #4D nails (attach base top to base frame)

Wood glue

1- 115 volt electric motor (should be at least 1/4 horse power. I used a 1750 R.P.M. motor with a 1/2" shaft. You may use something different depending on what you have on hand.)

1- 8" pulley 1/2" bore (countershaft outboard pulley)

2- 1 1/2" pulleys 1/2" bore (motor and countershaft pulleys)

1- 6" pulley 1/2" bore (crankshaft pulley)

2- pieces of 1 1/4" x 1/8" angle 6 1/2" long (motor mount rails)

2- pieces of 1" x 1/8" strap 4" long (motor rail spreaders)

4- 1/4-20 bolts 3/4" long (for assembling the motor mount spreaders to the motor mount rails)

2- pieces 1 1/4" x 1/8" angle 6 1/2" long (base rail)

1- piece of 1" x 1/8" strap 4" long (base rail spreader)

1- piece of 1" x 1/8" strap 2" long (slide arm stop bracket)

1- 5/16-18 bolt 1 1/2" long and nut (slide arm stop bolt and lock nut)

2- pieces of 1" x 1/8" strap 8" long (diagonal brace)

4- 1/4-20 bolts 1/2" long (for mounting motor mount to countershaft stand)

MATERIAL LIST CONTINUED

4- pillow block bearings with a 1/2" arbor (these can be of any brand but the resilient type often used for fans are not suitable. Solid mount bearings either bronze sleeve or ball will be ok.)

4- 1/4-20 bolts 1" long (for bolting pillow block bearings to countershaft stand)

2- pieces of 1 1/4" x 1/8" angle 10 1/2" long (countershaft stand side rail)

1- piece of 1" x 3/4" bar stock 4" long (slide and weight arm support pillar)

7- 5/8" O.D. 1/2" I.D. bronze bushings

4- 1/4-20 bolts 2" long with nuts, washers and lock washers (bolt pillow block bearings to base)

4- 1/2" shaft collars

2- 36" long pieces of 1/2" round rod suitable for use with bronze bushings (slide and weight arm)

1- 10 1/4" piece of 1/2" round rod suitable for use with bronze bushings (countershaft)

1- 8 3/4" piece of 1/2" round rod suitable for use with bronze bushings (crankshaft)

1- 9 1/2" piece of 1/2" round rod (connecting rod)

1- piece of 3/8" x 3/4" flat bar 4" long (crank arm)

1- 1/2" x 1" shoulder bolt (crank pin)

1- 3/8" - 16 nut (to secure shoulder bolt)

3- 1/4-20 set screws 1/4" long (to secure slide arm, weight arm, and crank arm in place)

2- 30" V belts

1- 1/2" clevis (to attach connecting rod to hacksaw frame)

1- 1 1/2" x 1/2" clevis pin (to secure clevis to hacksaw frame)

1- 3/32" x 1 5/8" hitch pin (hold clevis pin in place)

1- 1/2" flat washer (spacer between clevis and hitch pin)

1- 3/8" brass union tee flare fitting (connecting rod bearing)

MATERIAL LIST CONTINUED

1- piece of 3/8" x 2" flat bar 8 1/2" long (stabilizer post)

1- piece of 3/4" x 3/8" flat bar 25" long (saw frame)

2- pieces of 1/4" key stock 2" long (blade tension bolts)

2- pieces of 1/8" round rod 1/2" long (blade pins)

4- pieces of 1/4" key stock 3/4" long (blade tension bolt holding assembly)

1- piece of 3/4" x 3/4"- 1/8" strap (blade tension bolt holding assembly)

1- piece of 3/4" x 3/8" flat bar 3" long (clevis bushing housing)

2- pieces of 1/2" black pipe 3 3/4" long (slide arm bushing housing)

2- pieces of 1" x 1/8" strap 10" long (saw frame hanger brackets)

1- piece of 1/2" black pipe 10" long (saw frame stabilizer bushing housing)

1- 1/2" end cap (to cap open end of stabilizer housing)

1- 1/2" piece of 1/2" round 10" long (saw frame stabilizer rod)

TOOLS REQUIRED

Wood Saw (to cut the wood for the base)

Hammer (to assemble the base)

Hacksaw (to cut the metal parts)

Drill press with a 1/2" chuck (you may use a hand drill, but care must be taken to drill all holes straight)

Welder capable of 100 amps

Allen wrench set

Taps and dies 1/4-20, 1/2-20, 1/2-13

Wrenches, 7/16, 1/2, 9/16, 3/4

Assortment of drill bits from 1/8", to 7/8"

Vise grips

Bench vise

Torch

BUILDING THE BASE

To build the base frame cut two pieces of 2x4 lumber 33" long and two pieces 10" long. It will be necessary to cut a couple of notches in the frame for access to bolt the pillow block bearings and countershaft stand to the base. Refer to detail 5 on page 14 for notch size and locations. Place a little wood glue on each joint and nail the base frame together using 8D nails.

The base top is a piece of 3/4" plywood 36" long and 10" wide. Before it is nailed to the frame drill eight 1/4" holes in it. Four of these holes are for mounting the crankshaft pillow block bearings. The other four holes are for mounting the countershaft stand. I have placed a letter "c" by the holes for the countershaft stand and a letter "p" by the holes for the pillow block bearings. Refer to detail 6 on page 15. The dimensions given are for the pillow block bearings that I used. If you use different bearings the dimensions will have to be changed. It will also be necessary to cut a hole in the base top 1 1/2" wide and 7 1/2" long. The 6" crankshaft pulley will set in this hole. Once again, refer to detail 6 on page 15 for hole location. Place a little wood glue on top of the base frame. The notched side of the frame is the top side. Set the top on the base frame, align the edges and nail in place with #4D nails.

CHOOSING YOUR MOTOR AND DECIDING WHICH PULLEYS TO USE

The motor I used is 1/3 H.P. and runs at 1750 R.P.M.. It has a nema 48 frame. The holes on this particular frame are 3" between slot centers and 5" vertically. The rotation of the motor that I used is universal. I can cause the motor to run either clockwise, or counter clockwise, by switching two wires behind the removable service plate. Not all motors are reversible. Chances are you will have a motor on hand, but it will not be exactly like the one I used. That's OK, because if it has a different R.P.M. rating, all you have to do is change the reduction pulley sizes to gain the desired R.P.M. output. The motor you choose should have at least a 1/4 H.P. rating. If your motor mount frame is different, all you have to do is change the hole locations on the motor rails shown in detail 7 on page 16. As for the direction of the rotation of the shaft, I have found only a slight difference between clockwise and counter clockwise operation of the saw. Running in the counter clockwise direction the saw frame does not lift away from the work as much on the forward, or lift stroke. It also seems to cut heavier material a little better. Running in the clockwise direction it cuts lighter material a little better. If you have a motor that is reversible you will be able to run your own tests and decide which direction is better. Frankly, I don't think there is enough difference to matter. If the motor you choose runs clockwise it will be fine. If it runs counter clockwise that's OK too.

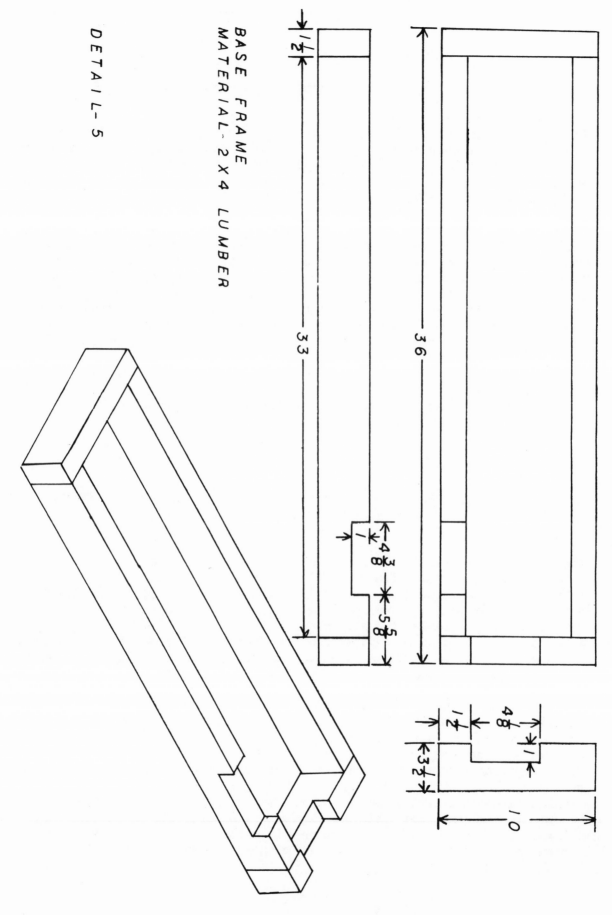

BASE FRAME
MATERIAL-2×4 LUMBER

DETAIL-5

14

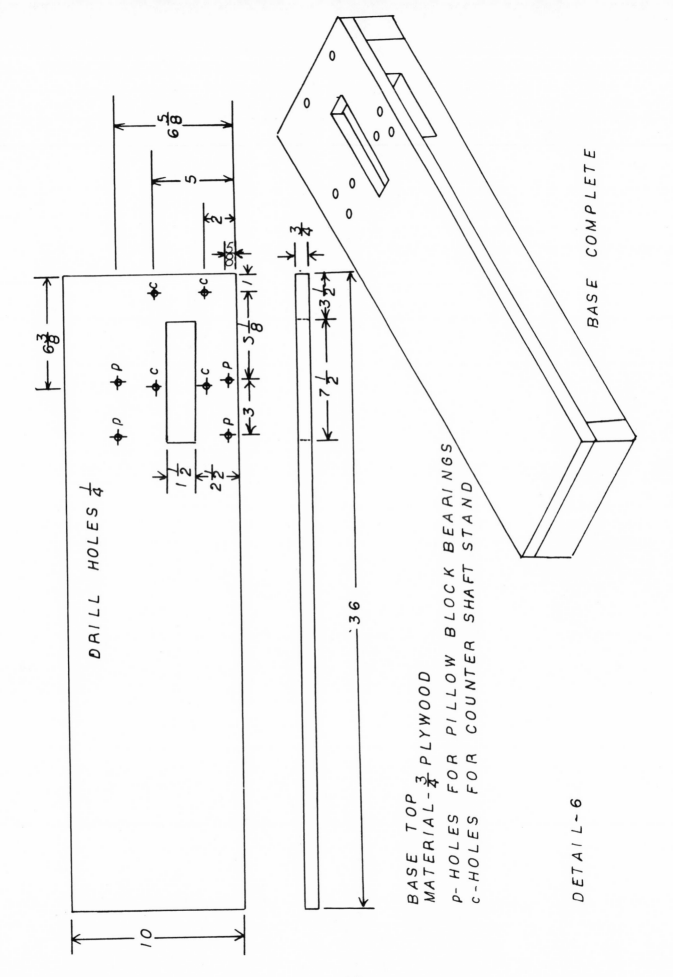

DRILL HOLES $\frac{1}{4}$

BASE TOP
MATERIAL - $\frac{3}{4}$ PLYWOOD

p - HOLES FOR PILLOW BLOCK BEARINGS
c - HOLES FOR COUNTER SHAFT STAND

BASE COMPLETE

DETAIL - 6

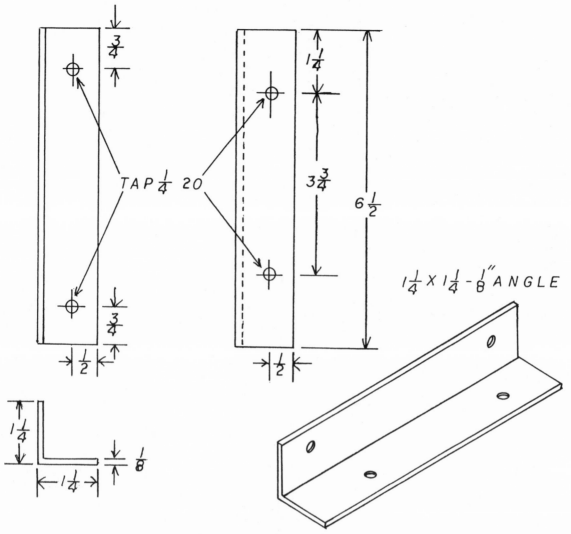

$TAP \frac{1}{4} \ 20$

$\frac{3}{4}$

$1\frac{1}{4}$

$3\frac{3}{4}$

$6\frac{1}{2}$

$\frac{3}{4}$

$\frac{1}{2}$

$\frac{1}{2}$

$1\frac{1}{4}$

$1\frac{1}{4}$

$\frac{1}{8}$

$1\frac{1}{4} \times 1\frac{1}{4} - \frac{1}{8}'' \ ANGLE$

MOTOR MOUNT RAIL
MAKE AN OPPOSING PAIR
DETAIL-7

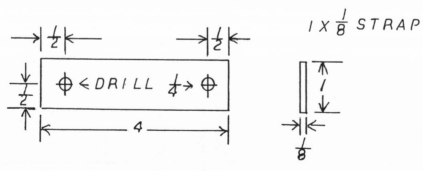

$\frac{1}{2}$

$\frac{1}{2}$

$\frac{1}{2}$

$\oplus \ \triangleleft DRILL \ \frac{1}{4} \triangleright \ \oplus$

4

$1 \times \frac{1}{8} \ STRAP$

1

$\frac{1}{8}$

RAIL SPREADER
MAKE 2
DETAIL-8

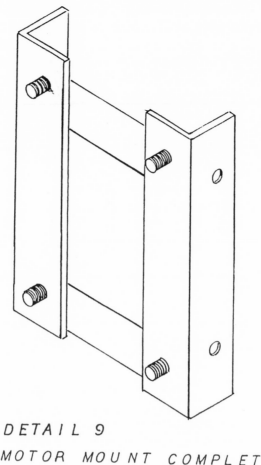

DETAIL 9

MOTOR MOUNT COMPLETE

I used the following method to choose the pulleys for the saw. I knew that I wanted the saw to travel at 60 strokes per minute. The first thing that we should know is that "A" pulleys have a pitch diameter that is 1/4" less than their outside diameter. I used an 8" outboard pulley on the countershaft and a 1 1/2" pulley on the motor shaft.

Divide 7.75 (the pitch diameter of the 8" outboard pulley) by 1.25 (the pitch diameter of the 1 1/2" motor pulley). This gives us a reduction ratio of 6.2 - 1. Divide 1750 (The R.P.M. rating of the motor I used) by 6.2 (the reduction ratio of the pulleys) 1750/6.2 = 282. This tells us that with this pulley configuration the countershaft is going to turn at 282 R.P.M..

On the countershaft I used a 1 1/2" pulley and on the crankshaft I used a 6" pulley. Using the same method as in the previous paragraph we can discover the crankshaft speed. To find the reduction ratio, divide 5.75 (the pitch diameter of the 6 1/2" crankshaft pulley) by 1.25 (the pitch diameter of the 1 1/2" countershaft pulley) 5.75/1.25 = 4.6 - 1. Divide the speed of the countershaft, which is 282 R.P.M., by the reduction ratio of 4.6-1, 282/4.6 = 61.3. Rounded off this gives us a saw speed of 61 strokes per minute.

BUILDING THE MOTOR MOUNT

The dimensions given for the motor mount, are for the motor that I used, and are stated as an example only. Chances are your motor mount will be different and you will have to adjust the location of the holes accordingly. We'll begin by making each piece necessary for the motor mount and then we'll assemble it.

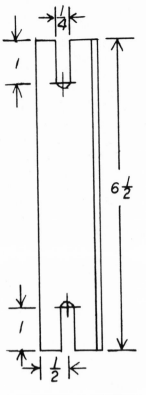

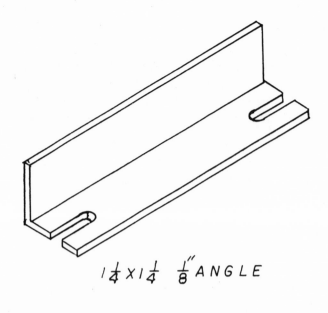

$1\frac{1}{4} \times 1\frac{1}{4}$ $\frac{1}{8}''$ ANGLE

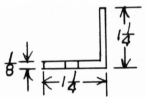

BASE RAIL MAKE 2
DETAIL -10

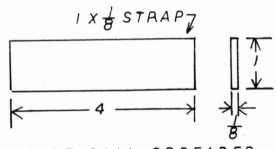

$1 \times \frac{1}{8}$ STRAP

4

BASE RAIL SPREADER
MAKE 1
DETAIL -11

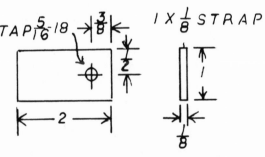

TAP $\frac{5}{16}$-18 $\frac{3}{8}$ $1 \times \frac{1}{8}$ STRAP

2

SLIDE ARM
STOP BRACKET
DETAIL -12

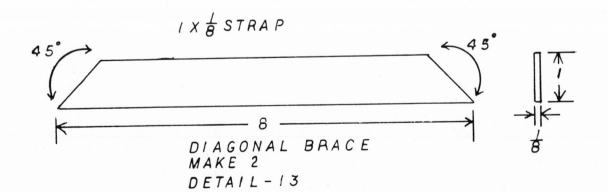

$1 \times \frac{1}{8}$ STRAP

45°   45°

8

$\frac{1}{8}$

DIAGONAL BRACE
MAKE 2
DETAIL -13

Make the motor mount rails first. These are two pieces of 1 1/4" x 1/8" angle 6 1/2" long. They are drilled and tapped 1/4-20 to correspond with the holes on your motor frame. See detail 7 on page 16. Two holes are also drilled and tapped 1/4-20 in each piece so that the motor mount can be attached to the countershaft.

The two motor rail spreaders are 1" x 1/8" strap 4" long, drilled 1/4" on center and 1/2" from each end. These are shown in detail 8 on page 16.

Assemble the motor mount by bolting the spreaders to the rails with 1/4-20 bolts 3/4" long. The bolts will extend through the rails 1/2" giving you studs for mounting the motor. See detail 9 on page 17 for a view of the motor mount complete.

BUILDING THE COUNTERSHAFT STAND

The base rails are first. Cut two pieces of 1 1/4" x 1/8" angle, 6 1/2" long. Drill and slot each end 1/4" wide, on center and 1" back from each end as shown in detail 10 on page 18.

The base rail spreader is a piece of 1" x 1/8" strap, 4" long. See detail 11 on page 18.

The slide arm stop bracket is a piece of 1" x 1/8" strap, 2" long. A hole is drilled and tapped 5/16 - 18 for the saw frame stop bolt. See detail 12 on page 18.

The diagonal braces are 2 pieces of 1" x 1/8" strap, 8" long, cut 45 degrees on each end. See detail 13 on page 18.

The side rails are last. We'll need to make one left and one right. Cut two pieces of 1 1/4" x 1/8" angle, 10 1/2" long. Detail 14 on page 20 shows dimensions for drilling and tapping. The holes that are tapped 1/4-20 are for mounting the countershaft pillow block bearings. The holes that are drilled 1/4", are for attaching the motor mount to the countershaft. The dimensions that I have given for drilling and tapping the holes for the pillow block bearings pertain only to the pillow block bearings that I used. I have included them here for an example only. If you use a different type, or size pillow block bearing, you will have to adjust the hole locations accordingly.

To assemble the countershaft stand first look at detail 15 on page 21 to see how it should look when it is assembled. Set the base rails on a flat surface suitable for welding. Set the left side rail against, and perpendicular to, the base rail. Make sure that the holes for mounting the pillow block bearings face the right direction as indicated in detail 15 on page 21. I used a machinist square to make sure that the side rail was perfectly perpendicular to the base rail. Clamp together with vise grips and weld. Repeat for the other side. Set the base rail spreader between the base rails as shown. Center and weld. Weld the slide arm stop bracket to the side rail.

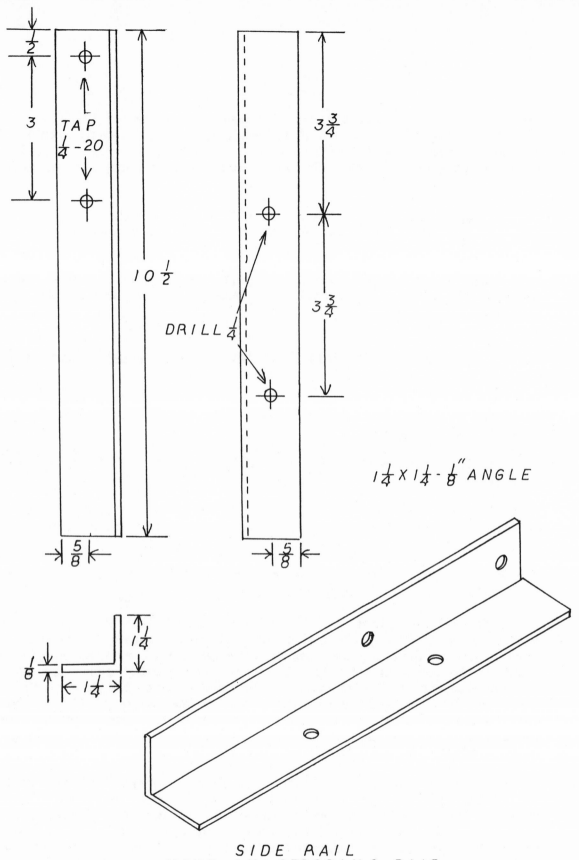

$\frac{1}{2}$

3

TAP $\frac{1}{4}$-20

$10\frac{1}{2}$

$\frac{5}{8}$

$3\frac{3}{4}$

DRILL $\frac{1}{4}$

$3\frac{3}{4}$

$\frac{5}{8}$

$1\frac{1}{4}$ X $1\frac{1}{4}$ - $\frac{1}{8}''$ ANGLE

$1\frac{1}{4}$

$\frac{1}{8}$

$1\frac{1}{4}$

SIDE RAIL
MAKE AN OPPOSING PAIR
DETAIL-14

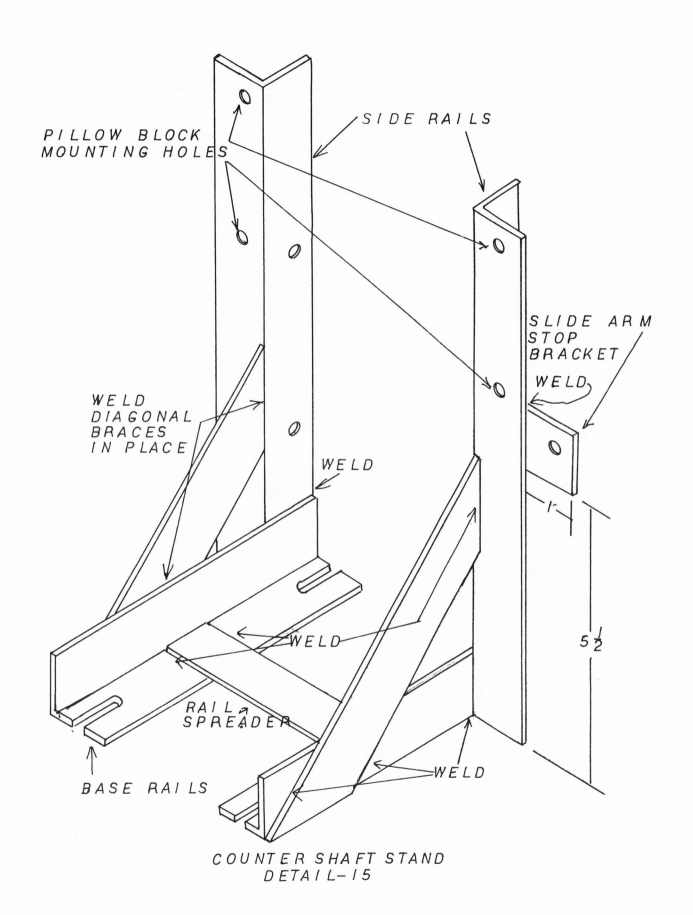

PILLOW BLOCK
MOUNTING HOLES

SIDE RAILS

SLIDE ARM
STOP
BRACKET

WELD

WELD
DIAGONAL
BRACES
IN PLACE

WELD

$5\frac{1}{2}$

WELD

RAIL
SPREADER

WELD

BASE RAILS

COUNTER SHAFT STAND
DETAIL-15

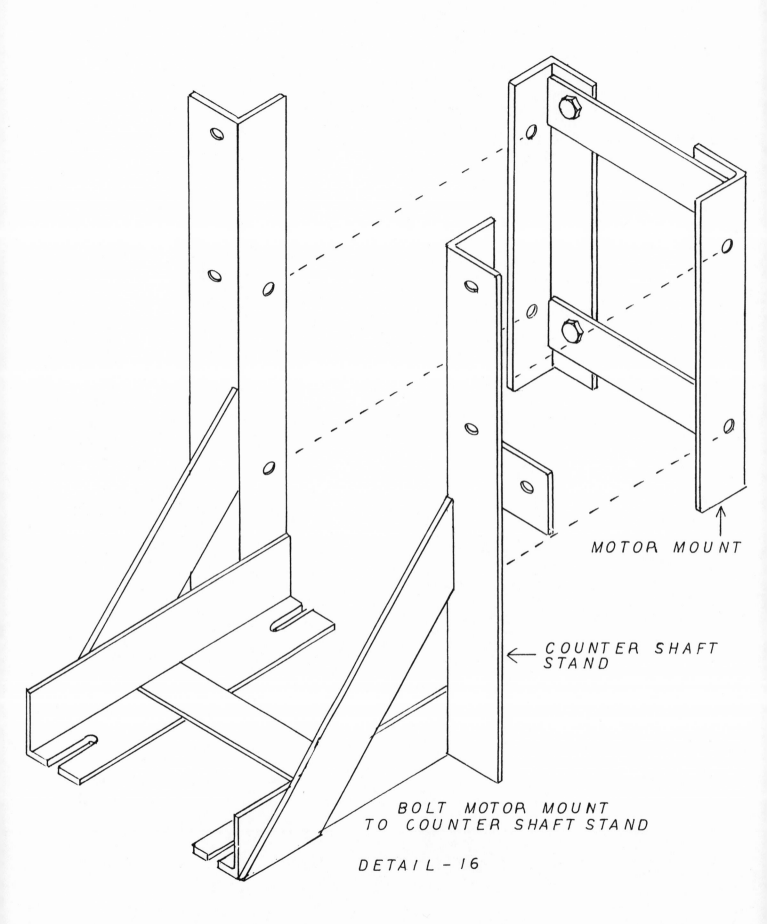

MOTOR MOUNT

COUNTER SHAFT
STAND

BOLT MOTOR MOUNT
TO COUNTER SHAFT STAND

DETAIL - 16

22

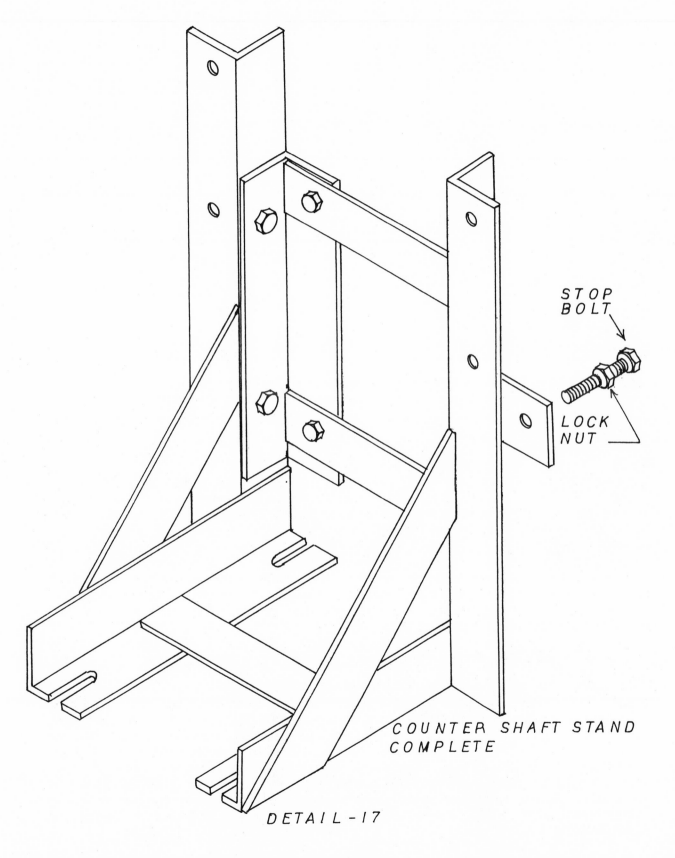

STOP
BOLT

LOCK
NUT

COUNTER SHAFT STAND
COMPLETE

DETAIL-17

23

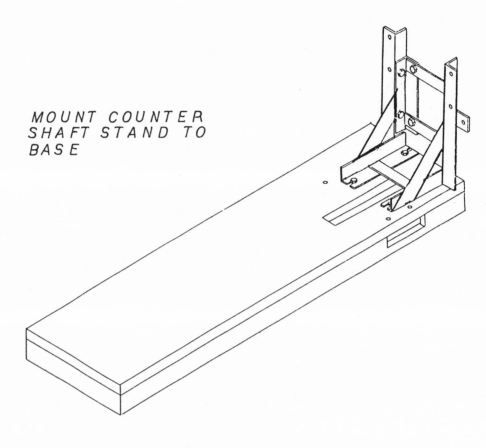

MOUNT COUNTER
SHAFT STAND TO
BASE

DETAIL-18

Screw the 5/16-18 x 1 1/2" stop bolt and lock nut into the hole in the stop
bracket. Weld both of the diagonal braces to the countershaft stand. See detail
15 on page 21. Bolt the motor mount assembly to the countershaft stand using 1/4-
20 x 1/2" bolts. See detail 16 on page 22. The counter shaft stand is now
complete.

Bolt the completed countershaft stand to the wooden base using 1/4-20 bolts 1
1/2" long. Be sure to use washers and lock washers. See detail 18 on page 24.
Fasten the motor to the motor mount studs using 1/4-20 nuts, washers, and lock
washers. See detail 19 on page 25.

ASSEMBLING THE COUNTERSHAFT

Bolt the pillow block bearings to the countershaft stand using 1/4-20 bolts 1"
long. I tried a couple of different types of pillow block bearings and found that
the resilient type, often used on fans, did not work well. Solid mount bearings,
either bronze sleeve or ball, work OK. You may use any brand you like. The one
I used was a model 7-500-5 1/2. It is manufactured by the Chicago Die Cast Co.,
9148 King St., Franklin Park, ILL 60131. I had no trouble finding them and they
were readily available at several hardware stores in my area. This style of
bearing is also available with arbor sizes up to 3/4" in case you want to use a
larger shaft than I did. See detail 20 on page 26 for a drawing of the pillow
block bearing that I used.

24

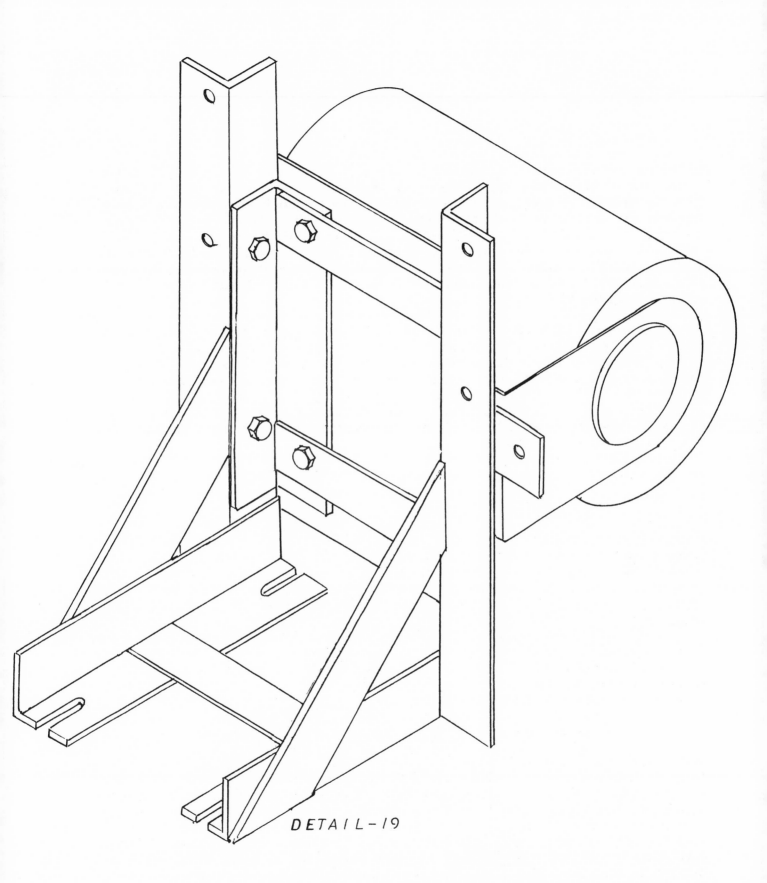

DETAIL-19

The slide arm and weight arm support pillar will need to be made next. It rides on the end of the countershaft. The slide arm and weight arm are both threaded into it. Be sure to drill and tap your holes straight in this part. It not only supports the entire saw frame assembly, it is the pivot point as well. Drilling these holes crooked could cause the saw to cut crooked. Material used is 1" x 3/4" mild steel bar stock. As shown in detail 21 on page 27, a 5/8" hole is drilled through it and a 5/8" O.D. 1/2" I.D. bronze bushing is pressed into the hole. Also drill and tap two holes 1/2-20 so that we can thread the slide and weight arms into it later.

The countershaft is a 10 1/4" piece of 1/2" round rod suitable for use with bronze bushings. After you cut it to length be sure to remove all burrs to prevent damage to the bushings. You can refer to detail 22 on page 28 as we assemble the countershaft. Don't grind the flat spots on the countershaft yet. We'll do that later. Insert the shaft through the pillow block bearing located on the left side of the countershaft stand. Slide one of the 1 1/2" pulleys on the shaft. Then slide a 1/2" collar onto the shaft. Insert the shaft through the other pillow block bearing.

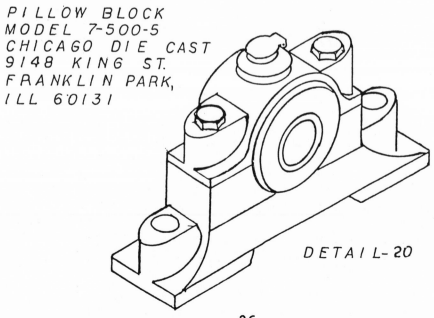

PILLOW BLOCK
MODEL 7-500-5
CHICAGO DIE CAST
9148 KING ST.
FRANKLIN PARK,
ILL 60131

DETAIL-20

26

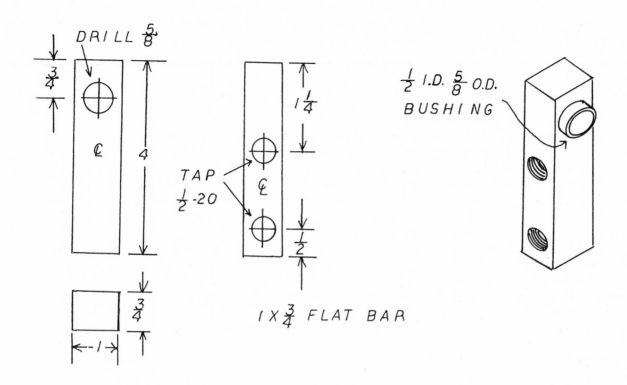

DRILL $\frac{5}{8}$

$\frac{3}{4}$

$\frac{C}{L}$

4

TAP $\frac{1}{2}$-20

$\frac{C}{L}$

$1\frac{1}{4}$

$\frac{1}{2}$

$\frac{3}{4}$

←—1—→

1 X $\frac{3}{4}$ FLAT BAR

$\frac{1}{2}$ I.D. $\frac{5}{8}$ O.D. BUSHING

SLIDE ARM AND WEIGHT ARM SUPPORT PILLAR
DETAIL-21

The shaft will extend out past the pillow block bearing 2 1/4". Slide the 3/8" long bronze spacer on the shaft. This spacer was made from a 1/2" bronze bushing trimmed to the length needed. Next place the slide arm support pillar on the shaft. Place a shaft collar on the end of the shaft. Place the 8" outboard pulley on the left end of the shaft. Now would also be a good time to place the 1 1/2" motor pulley on the end of the motor shaft. Do not tighten any of the set screws on the pulleys or shaft collars at this time. Detail 23 on page 29 shows the countershaft mounted to the stand. Detail 24 on Page 30 is a view of the counter shaft stand from outboard and motor pulley side.

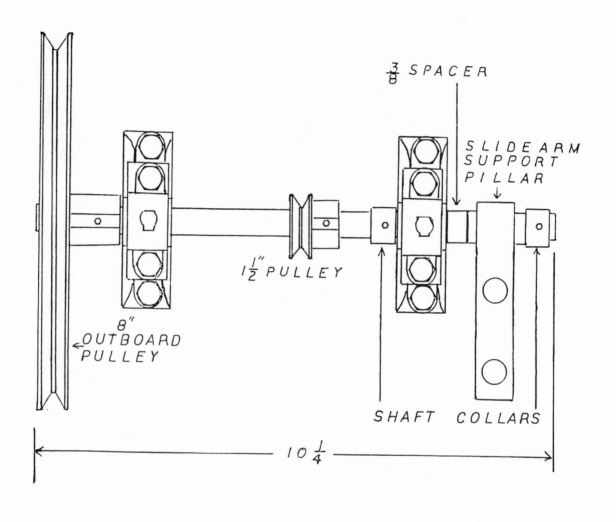

$\frac{3}{8}$ SPACER

SLIDE ARM
SUPPORT
PILLAR

$1\frac{1}{2}''$ PULLEY

$8''$
OUTBOARD
PULLEY

SHAFT COLLARS

$10\frac{1}{4}$

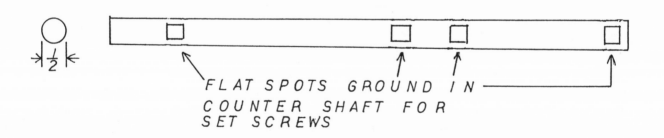

$\frac{1}{2}$

FLAT SPOTS GROUND IN
COUNTER SHAFT FOR
SET SCREWS

COUNTER SHAFT ASSEMBLY
DETAIL-22

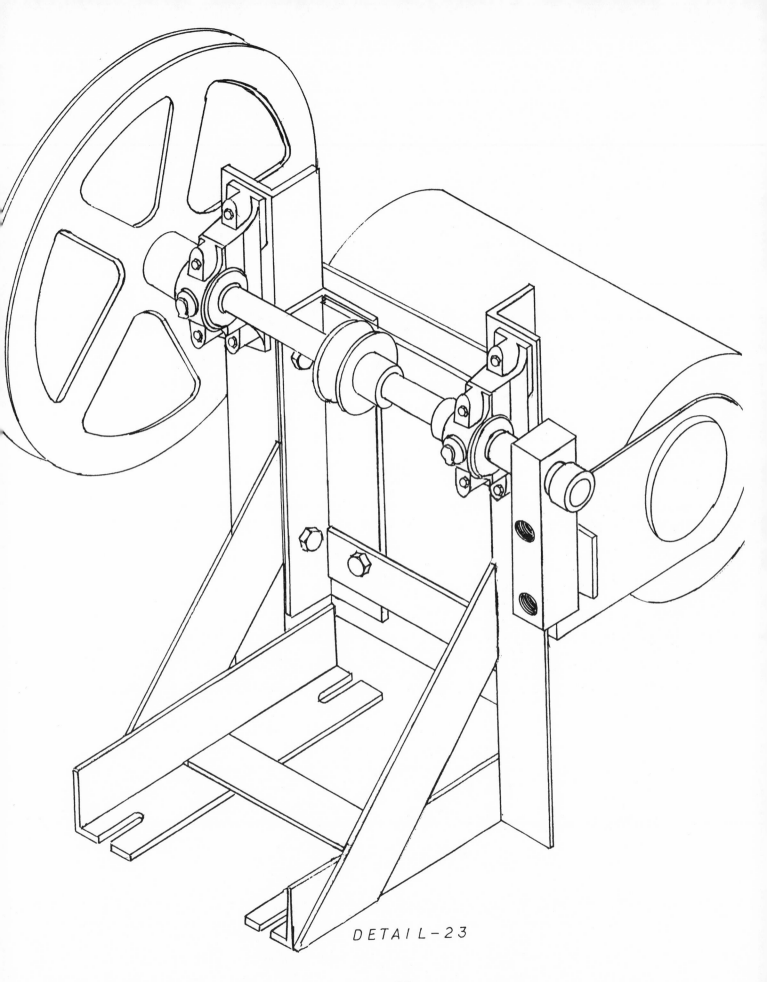

DETAIL-23

29

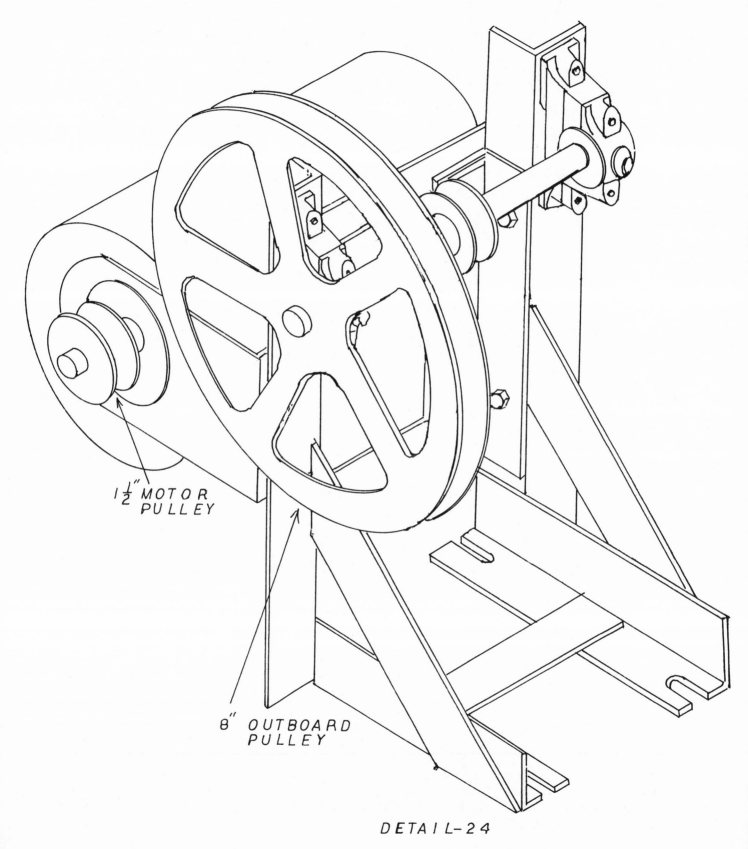

1½" MOTOR PULLEY

8" OUTBOARD PULLEY

DETAIL-24

30

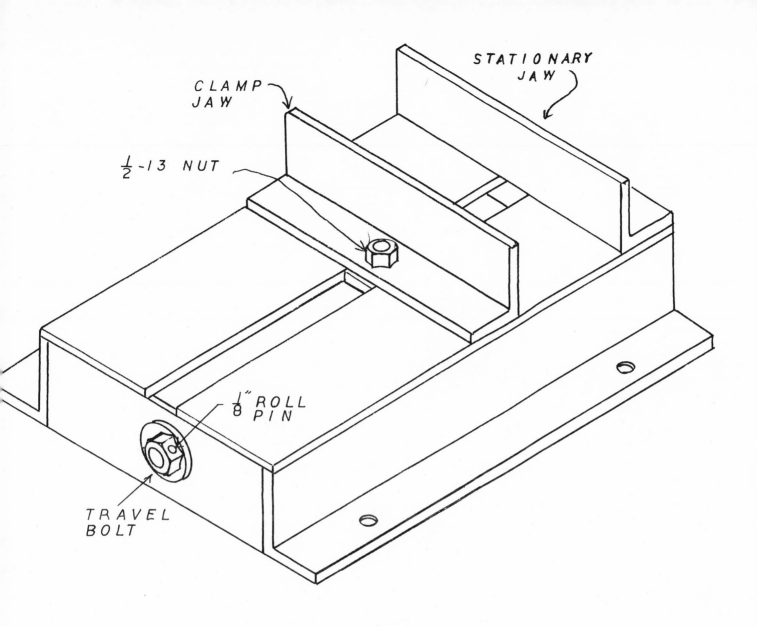

CLAMP
JAW

STATIONARY
JAW

½-13 NUT

1"/8 ROLL
PIN

TRAVEL
BOLT

VISE COMPLETE
DETAIL-25

INTRODUCTION TO BUILDING THE VISE

I think that now would be a good time to take a break from building the saw and start on the vise. The weight of the vise helps balance the base. When the vise is finished and bolted to the base a piece of material can be clamped in it giving us something to rest the saw frame on as we complete the project.

I had a 4" drill press vise on hand and I had planned to use it. After I looked it over I decided that it was to light weight for what I wanted and the jaws were only 1" deep. I also wanted something that I could adjust to different angles. I looked in the tool catalogs and found that there were some nice vises to choose from but the prices on the ones that I thought might work were pretty steep.

Not to be discouraged, I thought, I'm building a power hacksaw. How much harder can it be to build a vise to go along with it? So off to the scrap pile I went. I found quite a bit of 1/4" stuff and as result the vise is made entirely out of 1/4" steel angle and bar.

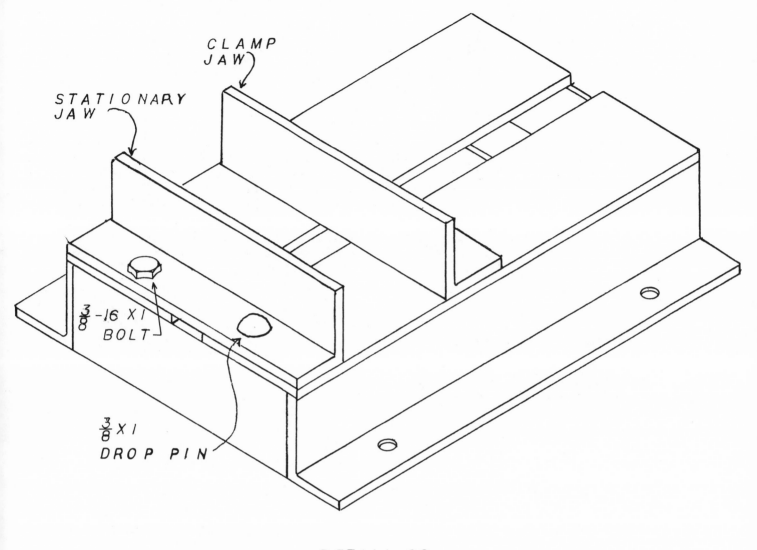

CLAMP JAW

STATIONARY JAW

$\frac{3}{8}$-16 X I
BOLT

$\frac{3}{8}$ X I
DROP PIN

DETAIL-26

I'm really glad that I decided to build my own vise and would certainly advise you to do the same. You will be well satisfied with it and save a $100.00 at the same time. The vise is easy and fun to build. The hardest part of the project is cutting the material by hand. It has turned out to be an excellent accessory and has fulfilled all of my needs up to this point.

The main body of the vise consists of the frame, the top and the jaws. The vise clamp jaw is operated by a 1/2" ratchet and 3/4" socket which turns a threaded rod, that I refer to in the text, as the screw shaft. The jaws of the vise open to 6 1/2" and they are 7" wide and 2" deep. The vise can be set up to hold material at any desired angle by removing the drop pin that holds the stationary jaw in place. You can then move the jaw to the angle position you desire. A hole will need to be drilled in the vise top at the desired angle so that the drop pin can be reinserted to hold the stationary jaw in place.

I used a 1/2-13 R.H. threaded rod for my screw shaft. It was easily found at the hardware store and it was not very expensive. I tried to find a place that would sell me L.H. threaded rod with an acme or square thread of 6 or 8 per inch. Neither was available in my area. I could have bought R.H. acme threaded rod, but the cost was quite a bit higher than the 1/2-13 that I already had. Because I used R.H. threaded rod the jaw action of the vise operates backwards from my other vises, but it didn't take me long to get used to it. At 13 threads per inch the jaw action was also slow, but I decided that I could live with that too.

VISE MATERIAL LIST

2- pieces of 1 1/2" x 2 - 1/4" angle 11 1/2" long. (side frame sections of vise)

2- pieces of 1 1/2" x 2" - 1/4" angle 6 1/4" long (front and rear frame sections of vise.

2- pieces of 1/4" x 3" flat bar (top section of vise)

2- pieces of 1 1/2 x 2" - 1/4" angle 7" long (stationary and clamp jaws)

1- piece of 1 1/2" x 2" - 1/4" angle 2 " long (clamp jaw travel nut)

1- piece of 1 1/2" x 13/16" - 1/4" thick mild steel. This can be cut from a scrap piece of 1/4" angle iron or flat bar (clamp jaw travel nut spacer)

1- 10" section of 1/2-13 threaded rod (vise screw shaft)

3- 1/2"-13 nuts

2- 1/2" flat washers

1- 1/2-13 bolt, 1- 3/8" drop pin, and 1- 3/8-16 bolt 1" long

2- 1/8 x 3/4 roll pins (to secure nuts to screw shaft)

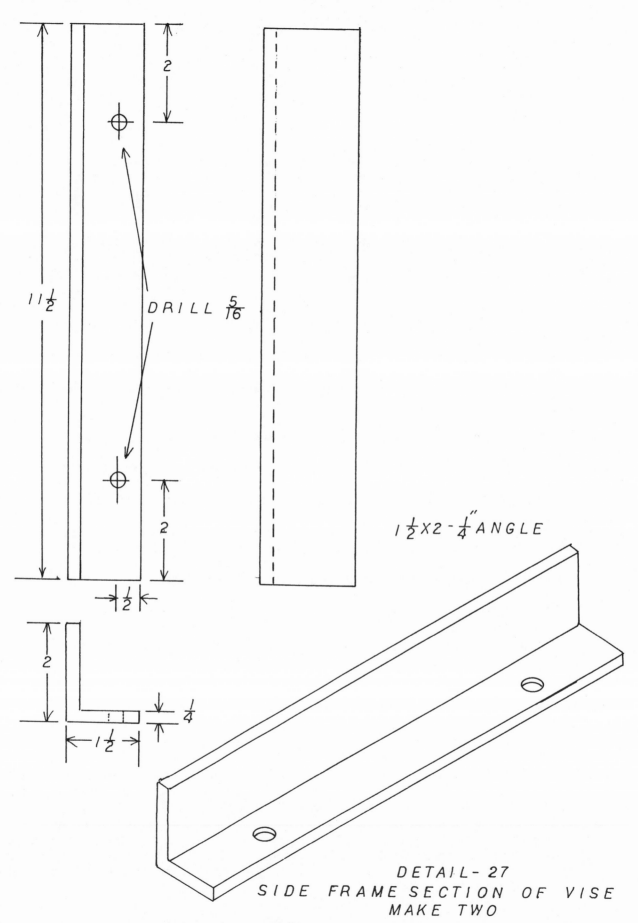

$DRILL \frac{5}{16}$

$11\frac{1}{2}$

2

2

$\frac{1}{2}$

2

$\frac{1}{4}$

$1\frac{1}{2}$

$1\frac{1}{2} X 2 - \frac{1}{4}'' ANGLE$

DETAIL-27
SIDE FRAME SECTION OF VISE
MAKE TWO

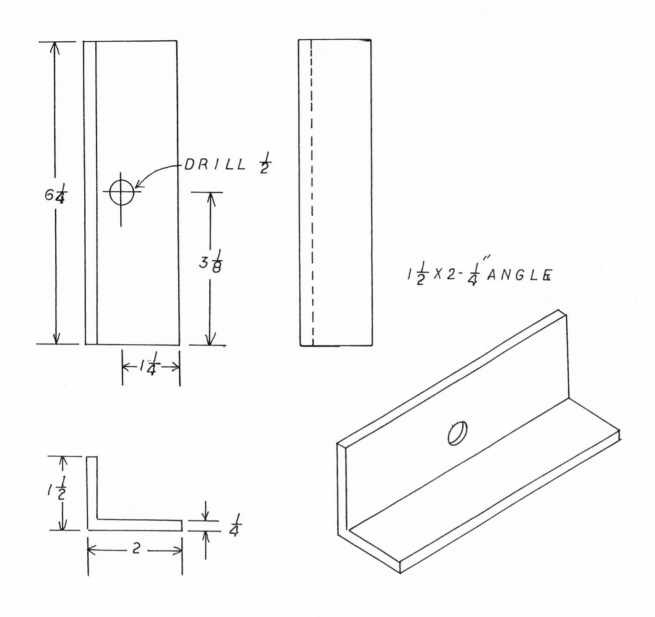

DRILL ½

$6\frac{1}{4}$

$3\frac{1}{8}$

$1\frac{1}{4}$

$1\frac{1}{2} \times 2 - \frac{1}{4}''$ ANGLE

$1\frac{1}{2}$

2

$\frac{1}{4}$

FRONT FRAME SECTION OF VISE
MAKE ONE
DETAIL-28

BUILDING THE VISE

Make the side sections of the vise frame first. Cut two pieces of 1 1/2" x 2" -
1/4" angle 11 1/2" long. Drill two 5/8" holes in each piece as shown in detail
27 on page 34. These are the mounting holes.

Cut two pieces of 1 1/2" x 2" - 1/4" angle, 6 1/4" long. Drill a 1/2" hole in one
of these pieces as shown in detail 28 on page 35. This is the front frame section
of the vise. The other piece is left alone and is the rear frame section of the
vise. See detail 29 on page 36.

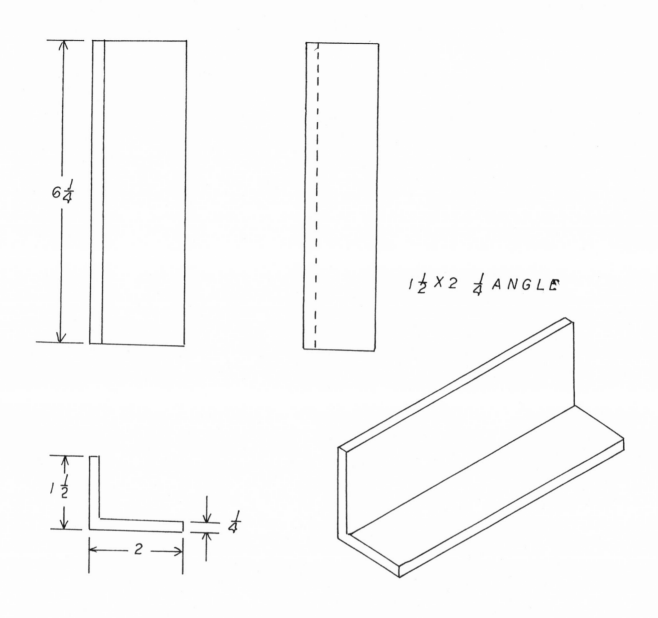

$1\frac{1}{2} X 2 \frac{1}{4}$ ANGLE

REAR FRAME SECTION OF VISE
MAKE ONE
DETAIL- 29

The vise frame assembled is shown in detail 30 on page 37. Place the two side frame sections on a flat surface suitable for welding. Notice how the angle section, with the mounting holes, faces out. Place the front and rear frame sections of the vise together with the side sections. Notice how the angled sections, of the front and rear frame sections, face inside the frame. Also make sure the front frame section is placed so that the hole for the vise travel bolt is in the proper place. When everything is set weld the corners together.

Cut two pieces of 1/4" x 3" flat bar 11 1/2" long. These will form the top section of the vise. Drill a 3/8" hole in one end of each piece, 5/8" from the end and centered. See detail 31 on page 38. Set the two top pieces on top of the vise frame. Align each piece with the outside edge of the frame.

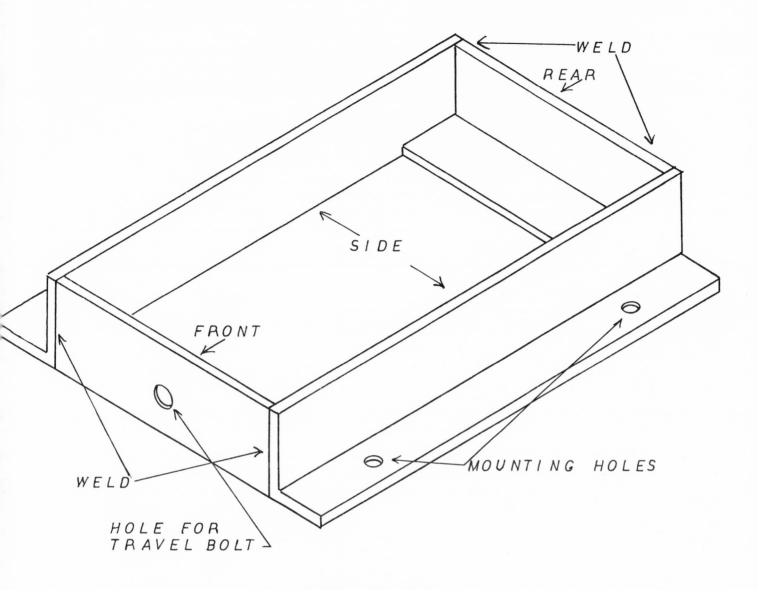

WELD

REAR

SIDE

FRONT

WELD

HOLE FOR
TRAVEL BOLT

MOUNTING HOLES

VISE FRAME
DETAIL-30

This should leave a space down the middle of approximately 7/8". The vise travel nut spacer will set in this space. Weld the two top sections to the frame section of the vise. See detail 32 on page 39. Weld on the outside edge only. It is not necessary to run a solid weld . I ran a 1/2" long weld, about every 2", all around the vise. This completes the main body of the vise.

Detail 34 on page 40 shows the dimensions for the travel nut. The travel nut is a piece of 1 1/2" x 2" - 1/4" angle 2" long. 1/8" is trimmed off the 2" side of this angle giving it a measurement of 1 7/8". We do this to give it clearance.

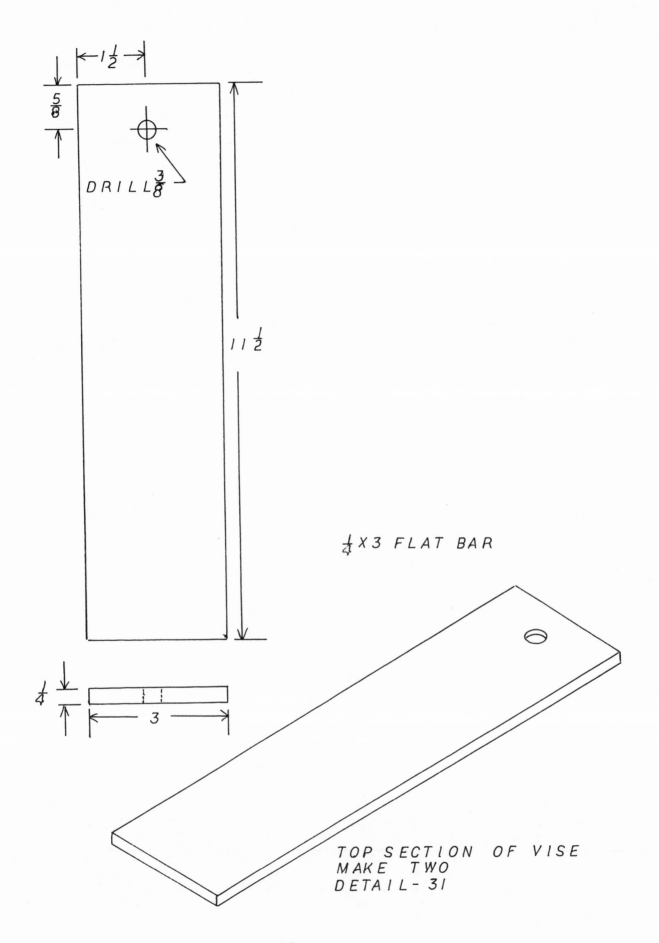

$1\frac{1}{2}$

$\frac{5}{8}$

DRILL $\frac{3}{8}$

$11\frac{1}{2}$

$\frac{1}{4}$ X 3 FLAT BAR

$\frac{1}{4}$

3

TOP SECTION OF VISE
MAKE TWO
DETAIL - 31

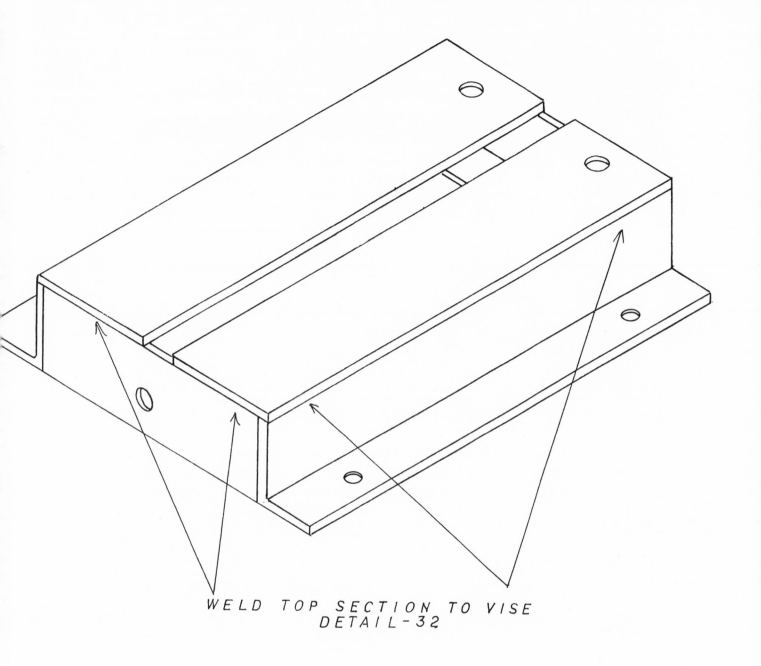

WELD TOP SECTION TO VISE
DETAIL-32

A hole is also drilled and tapped 1/2-13 in this same 1 7/8" side of the angle. The travel bolt threads through this hole. On the 1 1/2" side a 1/2" hole is drilled. This hole is used to mount the clamp jaw in place. By now it should be plain to see how the vise works. As you turn the screw shaft the travel nut moves back and forth on the threaded rod depending on which direction you turn it. This same travel nut is attached to the clamp jaw. So as you turn the screw shaft and move the travel nut the clamp jaw follows it.

THREAD $\frac{1}{2}$-13 $\frac{1}{2}$ THREADED ROD

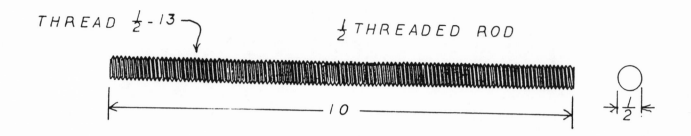

|← —————————— 10 —————————— →| $\frac{1}{2}$

CLAMP JAW TRAVEL BOLT
DETAIL-33

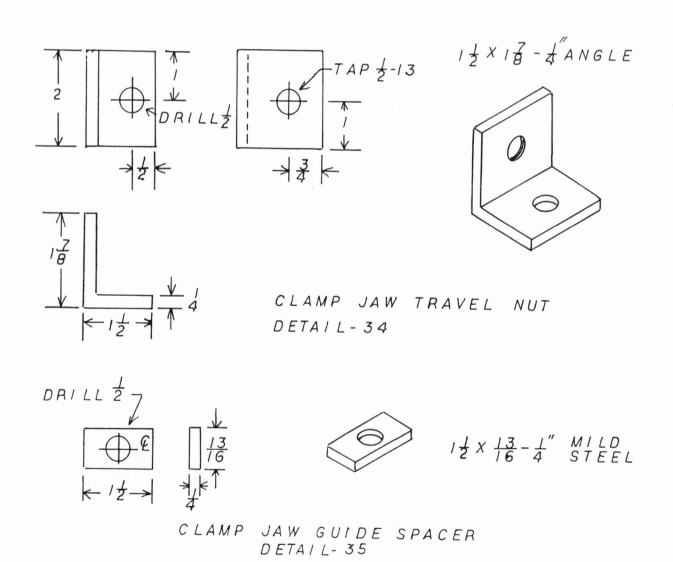

DRILL $\frac{1}{2}$ TAP $\frac{1}{2}$-13 $1\frac{1}{2}$ X $1\frac{7}{8}$ - $\frac{1}{4}''$ ANGLE

2    $\frac{1}{2}$ $\frac{3}{4}$

$1\frac{7}{8}$ $1\frac{1}{2}$ $\frac{1}{4}$

CLAMP JAW TRAVEL NUT
DETAIL-34

DRILL $\frac{1}{2}$

$1\frac{1}{2}$ $\frac{13}{16}$ $\frac{1}{4}$ $1\frac{1}{2}$ X $\frac{13}{16}$ - $\frac{1}{4}''$ MILD STEEL

CLAMP JAW GUIDE SPACER
DETAIL-35

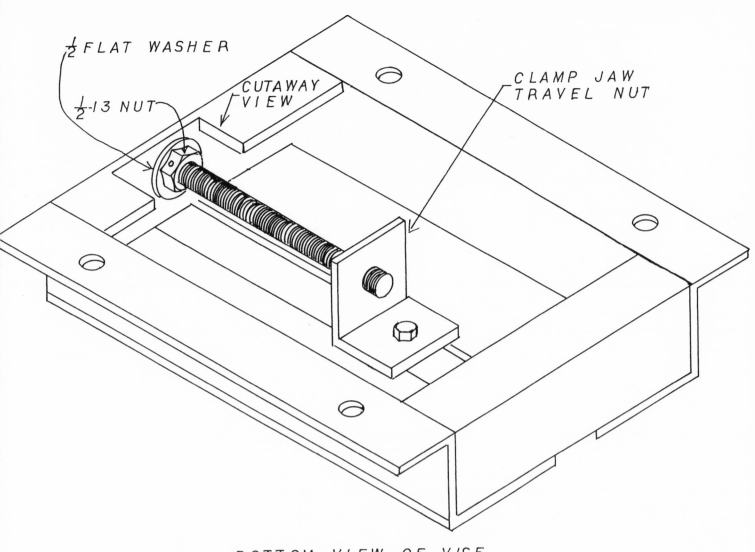

$\frac{1}{2}$ FLAT WASHER

$\frac{1}{2}$-13 NUT

CUTAWAY VIEW

CLAMP JAW TRAVEL NUT

BOTTOM VIEW OF VISE
SHOWING TRAVEL ASSEMBLY
DETAIL-36

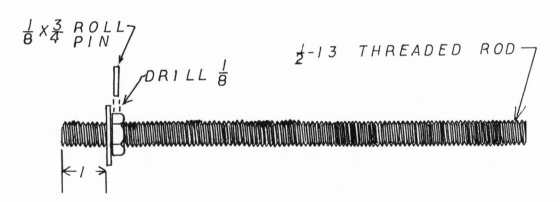

$\frac{1}{8} \times \frac{3}{4}$ ROLL PIN

DRILL $\frac{1}{8}$

$\frac{1}{2}$-13 THREADED ROD

|← 1 →|

DETAIL-37

41

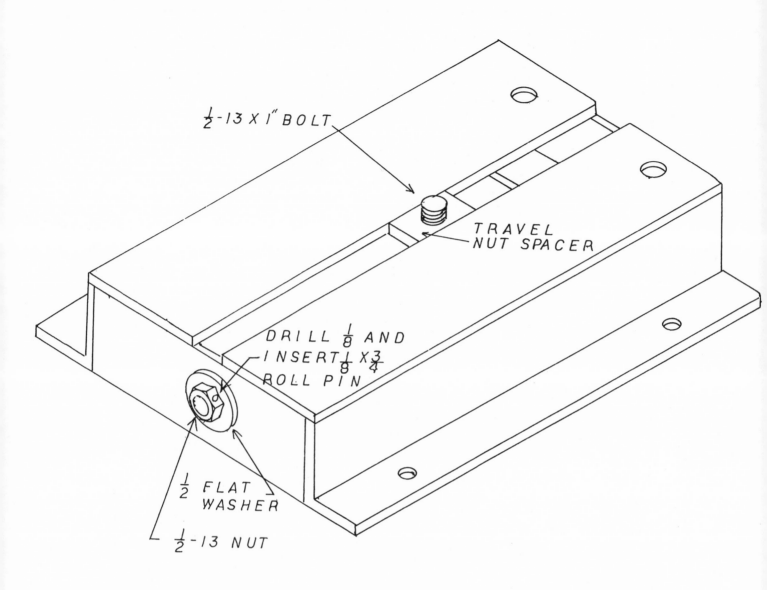

$\frac{1}{2}$-13 X 1" BOLT

TRAVEL
NUT SPACER

DRILL $\frac{1}{8}$ AND
INSERT $\frac{1}{8}$ X $\frac{3}{4}$
ROLL PIN

$\frac{1}{2}$ FLAT
WASHER

$\frac{1}{2}$-13 NUT

DETAIL-38

We'll need a piece of 1/2" threaded rod 10" long for the screw shaft. I used 1/2-13 R. H. threaded rod because it was inexpensive and easy to find. As discussed earlier if you have something that will work better by all means use it. See detail 33 on page 40. Thread a 1/2"-13 nut on one end of the 10" screw shaft. Allow 1 1/8" of the shaft to extend past the nut. Drill a 1/8" hole through the nut and the screw shaft. Drive a 1/8" x 3/4" roll pin through the 1/8" hole that you just drilled. This secures the nut to the screw shaft. See detail 37 on page 41. Place a 1/2" flat washer against the nut. Thread the vise travel nut on the other end of the screw shaft. Turn the vise over so that you are looking at the bottom side of it. Refer to detail 36 on page 41. Insert the screw shaft through the 1/2" hole in the front of the vise frame. The shaft will extend out in front of the vise 5/8". Turn the vise back over so that you are looking at the top. Refer to detail 38 on page 42. Place a 1/2" flat washer and a 1/2-13 nut on the end of the screw shaft. Tighten only enough to take up the slack and still allow free movement of the screw shaft. Drill an 1/8" hole through the nut and screw shaft. Drive an 1/8" x 3/4" roll pin into the hole that you just drilled. This secures the nut to the screw shaft.

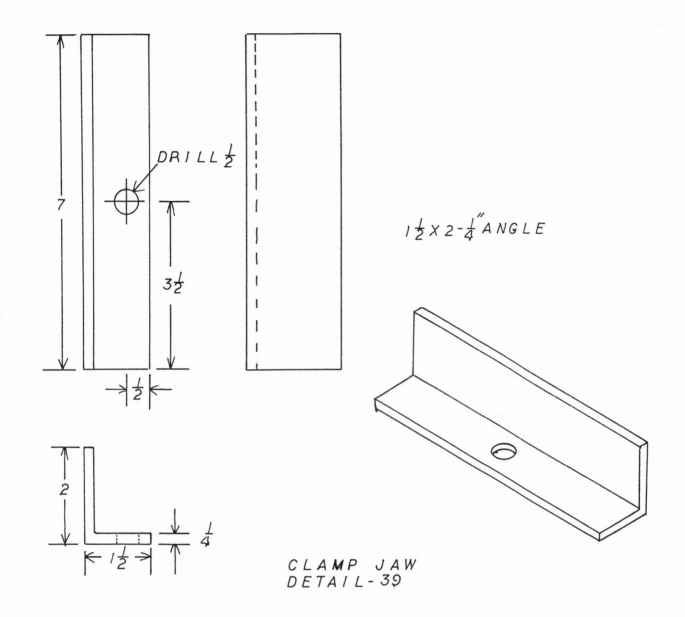

DRILL $\frac{1}{2}$

7

$3\frac{1}{2}$

$\frac{1}{2}$

$1\frac{1}{2} X 2-\frac{1}{4}'' ANGLE$

2

$\frac{1}{4}$

$1\frac{1}{2}$

CLAMP JAW
DETAIL-39

Cut a piece of 3/4" x 1 1/2" - 1/4" thick mild steel. Center from both ends and drill a 1/2" hole. This will be the travel nut spacer. See detail 35 on page 40. Set the travel nut spacer in the slot on top of the travel nut. See detail 38 on page 42. A 1/2 - 13 bolt 1" long is inserted through the hole in the travel nut and travel nut spacer. The bolt should be inserted from the bottom side. We are now ready to make the jaws of the vise.

The jaws of the vise are made from two pieces of 1 1/2" x 2" -1/4" angle 7" long. The clamp jaw is shown in detail 39 on page 43. Drill a 1/2" hole in it to the dimensions shown. It is bolted to the travel nut with a 1/2 - 13 x 1" bolt and nut. Tighten only enough to take up the slack. See detail 35 on page 31. Operate the vise screw shaft to make sure the clamp jaw still travels smoothly.The stationary jaw is shown in detail 40 on page 44. Drill two 3/8" holes in it to the dimensions shown. Attach the stationary jaw to the vise using a 3/8-16 bolt 1" long on one side and a 3/8" x 1 drop pin on the other side. See detail 26 on page 32.

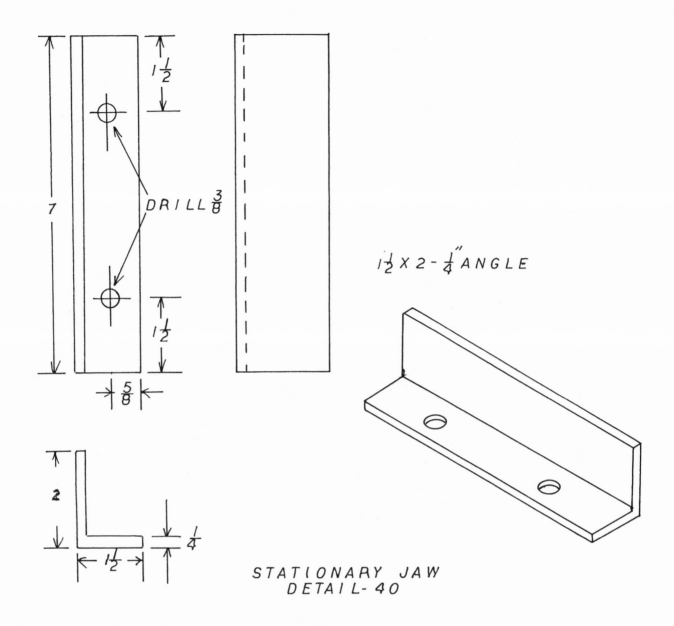

DRILL $\frac{3}{8}$

$1\frac{1}{2}$

$1\frac{1}{2}$

7

$\frac{5}{8}$

$1\frac{1}{2} \times 2 - \frac{1}{4}"$ ANGLE

2

$1\frac{1}{2}$

$\frac{1}{4}$

STATIONARY JAW
DETAIL-40

Congratulations! You have just completed building your own vise. Now that the vise is complete mount it to the wooden base using 5/16" x 1" lag bolts. See detail 41 on page 45. To operate the vise I used a 1/2" ratchet and a 3/4" socket. If you want to make any angle cuts with your saw, it's a simple matter to make the stationary clamp jaw of your vise adjustable. Set an adjustable protractor on the side edge of your vise. Pull the drop pin and swing the stationary jaw to the angle of your choice. Mark the spot on the vise top that coincides with the hole in the stationary jaw. Drill a 3/8" hole at the marked spot. Insert the drop pin into the hole securing the stationary jaw at this angle. Insert the material that you want to cut in the vise. Tighten the vise. The saw will cut your material at the angle set up.

44

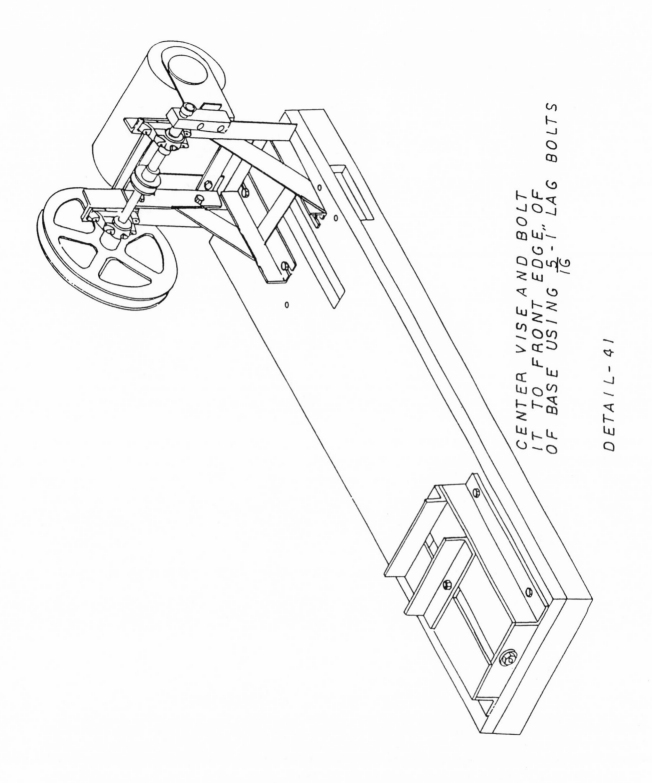

CENTER VISE AND BOLT
IT TO FRONT EDGE. OF
OF BASE USING $\frac{5}{16}$-1" LAG BOLTS

DETAIL-41

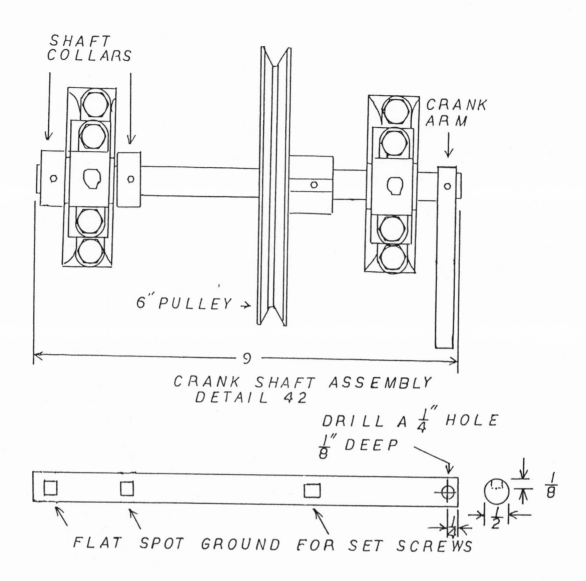

SHAFT COLLARS

CRANK ARM

6" PULLEY →

9

CRANK SHAFT ASSEMBLY
DETAIL 42

DRILL A $\frac{1}{4}$" HOLE
$\frac{1}{8}$" DEEP

$\frac{1}{8}$

$\frac{1}{2}$

$\frac{1}{4}$

FLAT SPOT GROUND FOR SET SCREWS

CRANK SHAFT
DETAIL 43

THE CRANKSHAFT ASSEMBLY

As we begin installing the crankshaft assembly on the wooden base, you may refer to detail 43, on page 46 for clarification. Detail 45, on page 48 shows the crank shaft mounted to the base. First bolt the pillow block bearings to the base. Use 1/4-20 bolts, 2" long, washers and lock washers. Cut a piece of 1/2" round rod, 9" long, suitable for use with bronze bushings. This will be the crankshaft. Be sure to debur the ends. In order to prevent the crank arm from slipping on the crankshaft, it will be necessary to drill a 1/4" hole, 1/8" deep in one end of the crankshaft. The crank arm set screw, sets in this hole. Detail 43, on page 46 clarifies this. Slide the shaft into the first pillow block bearing located on the crank arm side of the base.

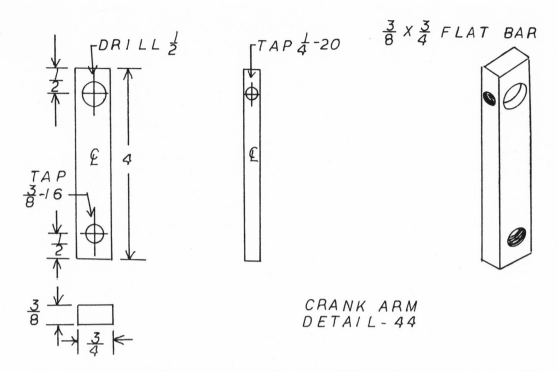

DRILL $\frac{1}{2}$

TAP $\frac{1}{4}$-20

$\frac{3}{8}$ X $\frac{3}{4}$ FLAT BAR

TAP $\frac{3}{8}$-16

4

$\frac{3}{8}$

$\frac{3}{4}$

CRANK ARM
DETAIL - 44

Set the 6" crankshaft pulley into the recess that has been cut out in the base. Slide the crankshaft through the pulley. Slide a shaft collar on and then slide the shaft through the other pillow block bearing. Place the other shaft collar on the end of the crankshaft. The crankshaft will extend past the pillow block bearing on the crank arm side 3/4". This gives us room to mount the crank arm on the crankshaft.

The crank arm is a piece of 3/8" x 3/4" flat bar 4" long. Refer to detail 44 on page 47. Drill a 1/2" hole on one end. This end of the crank arm will go on the crankshaft. It will also be necessary to drill and tap a 1/4-20 hole through the side of this 1/2" hole for a set screw. On the other end of the crank arm drill and tap a 3/8-16 hole. The crank pin will thread into this hole. Set the crank arm on the crankshaft.

Now would be a good time to go back and prepare the countershaft and crankshaft so that the set screws can be tightened. In order to tighten the set screws a flat spot must be ground on the shaft at the point where the set screw comes in contact with it. This prevents the pulleys and shaft collars from slipping and creating burrs on the shaft which could damage the bronze bushings. Simply line the pulleys up so that they are straight with each other, mark the spot and file or grind a flat spot on the shaft at the marked point. Do the same thing with the shaft collars.

It would also be a good idea to install the "V" belts now before we tighten the set screws. I used 30" "V" belts to drive both the countershaft and crankshaft. You may require a different size belt so it would be a good idea for you to measure to be sure of the size belt you need before you buy. To find which size belt you need measure the total distance over both pulleys. This measurement will give you the size belt you need in inches. Slide the countershaft and drive shaft over to one side. Place the belts in position. Slide the shafts back in position. Line up the pulleys and tighten all set screws including the shaft collar set

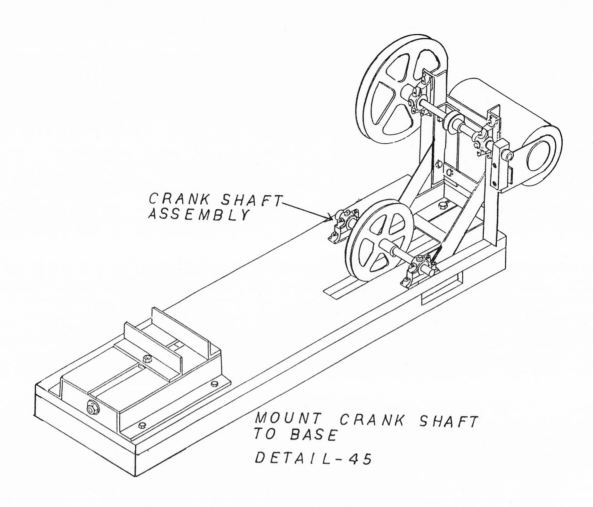

CRANK SHAFT
ASSEMBLY

MOUNT CRANK SHAFT
TO BASE
DETAIL - 45

screws. Mount the belts on the pulleys. The crankshaft belt tension is adjusted by loosening the countershaft stand mounting bolts and sliding the stand forward, or backward as required. The motor belt tension is adjusted by loosening the motor mount nuts and sliding the motor up, or down as required. New "V" belts have a tendency to stretch when they are first used. It will be necessary to adjust the belt tension a few times, when you first start using your saw, to correct any belt slipping problems.

BUILDING THE HACKSAW FRAME

On the first power hacksaw that I built, I used a standard hand hacksaw frame instead of building my own. It did not give satisfactory performance. The frame was weak and would not hold a blade tight enough to support it during the cut. So, even though it is a bit more work, I think you should build your own frame.

Cut a piece of 3/4" x 3/8" flat bar 26" long. Refer to detail 46 on page 49 for the saw frame layout. Measure 6 3/4" back from each end and make a mark. Clamp the flat bar in a vise and heat one of the marked sections to a bright red. Then bend it slowly to a 90 degree angle. It will be necessary to stop and reheat the flat bar a couple of times to complete the bend. Be sure to allow the heated section to cool and then bend the other leg of the frame in the same manner. Care must be taken to be sure that the legs of the saw frame remain straight, and parallel to each other, as this will determine how straight the saw will cut. Trim the length of the legs of the saw frame to 5 1/4" as shown.

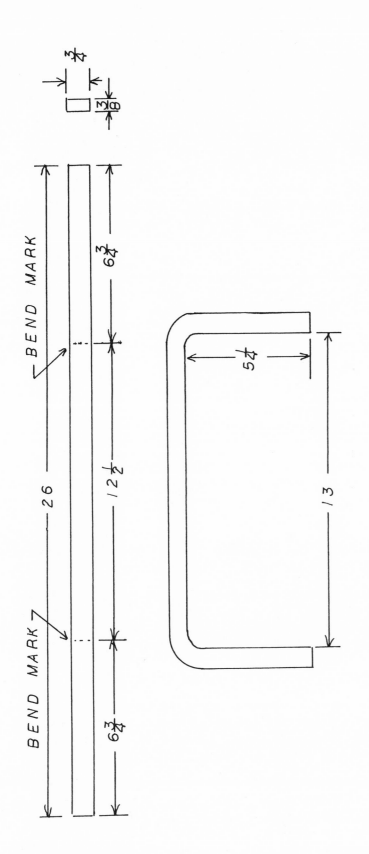

FORMING THE HACKSAW FRAME
MATERIAL: $\frac{3}{8}$ X $\frac{3}{4}$ FLAT BAR
HEAT AREA AT BEND MARK AND
BEND MATERIAL TO FORM FRAME

DETAIL- 46

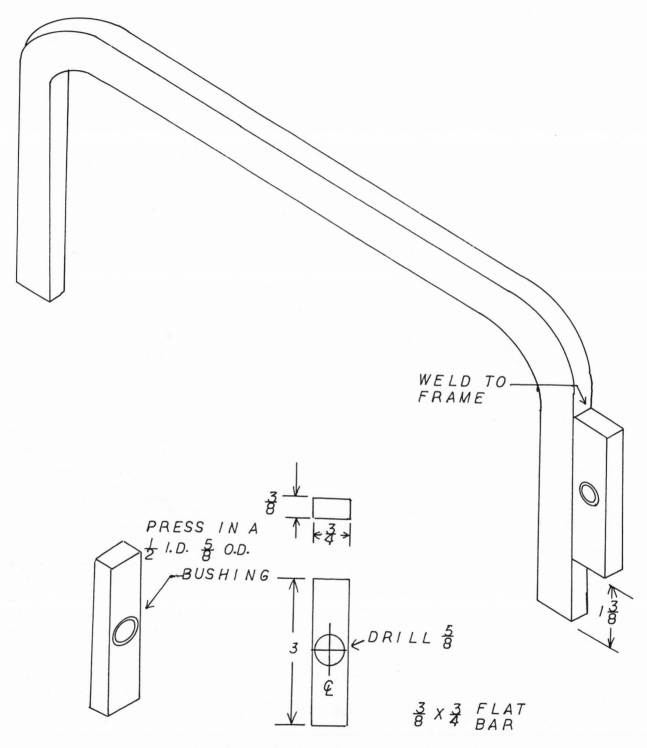

WELD TO FRAME

$\frac{3}{8}$

$\frac{3}{4}$

$1\frac{3}{8}$

PRESS IN A $\frac{1}{2}$ I.D. $\frac{5}{8}$ O.D. BUSHING

DRILL $\frac{5}{8}$

3

℄

$\frac{3}{8}$ X $\frac{3}{4}$ FLAT BAR

CLEVIS BUSHING

DETAIL 47

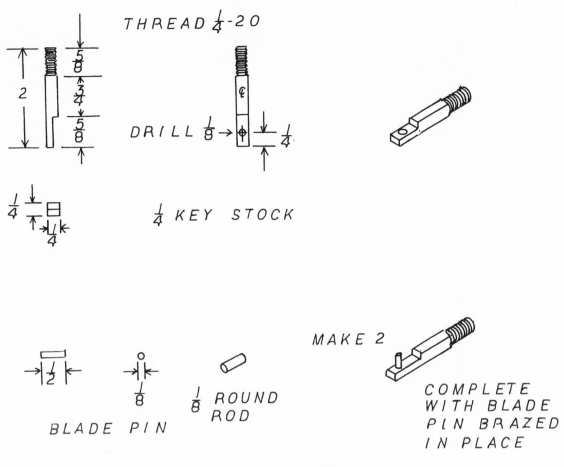

THREAD 1/4-20

DRILL 1/8 →

2

5/8
3/4
5/8

1/4

1/4 KEY STOCK

1/4 | 1/4

1/2

1/8

BLADE PIN

1/8 ROUND ROD

MAKE 2

COMPLETE WITH BLADE PIN BRAZED IN PLACE

DETAIL-48
BLADE PIN TENSION BOLT

We can now attach the clevis bushing to the saw frame. Cut a piece of 3/4" x 3/8" flat bar 3" long. Drill a 5/8" hole on center and press a 3/8"long, 5/8" O.D., 1/2" I.D., bronze bushing into this hole as shown in detail 47 on page 50. Place the completed clevis bushing assembly against the leg of the saw frame 1 3/8" up from the bottom edge of the leg. Weld it in place. Be sure to protect the bushing from weld splatter. This is the point at which the clevis hooks to the saw frame.

A means of attaching the saw blade to the frame must now be added. These will be referred to as blade tension bolts. They will consist of two pieces of 1/4" key stock each piece being 2" long. You may refer to detail 48 on page 51 as we discuss these. They are each threaded on one end 1/4-20 X 5/8". In order to thread the key stock 1/4 - 20 it is necessary to round the corners off just a little with a file or bench grinder so that you can get the die started. The center section of the tension bolt remains 1/4" square. This section is 3/4" long. The other end, which is 5/8" long, is ground down until it is 1/8" thick. This forms a notch for the blade to set. Also take note of the two pieces of 1/8" round rod that are 1/2" long. These are referred to as the blade pins. A 1/2" section of an 8 penny nail made each pin. Drill a 1/8" hole in the notched side of each tension bolt as shown. Insert the 1/2" section of 1/8" round rod into this hole. The pin should extend 3/8" up from the notched side and be flush with the other side. Braze the pin in place on the bottom or flush side to secure. Do not braze on the side that extends up because the saw blade sets flush against the tension bolt.

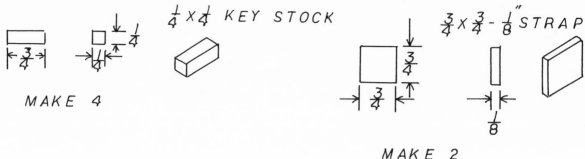

MAKE 4

$\frac{1}{4}$ X $\frac{1}{4}$ KEY STOCK

$\frac{3}{4}$ X $\frac{3}{4}$ - $\frac{1}{8}$" STRAP

MAKE 2

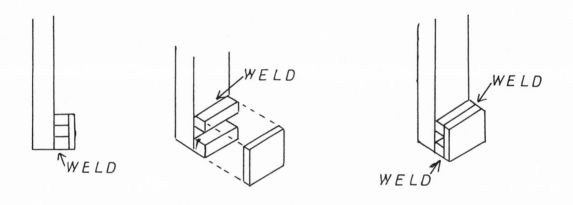

WELD

WELD

WELD

WELD

BLADE TENSION BOLT
HOLDING ASSEMBLY
DETAIL-49

A method of holding the tension bolts to the frame is shown in detail 49 on page 52 and may be referred to as we make the parts. Cut four pieces of 1/4" key stock 3/4" long and two pieces of 3/4" x 3/4" - 1/8" strap. Place one of the pieces of 1/4" key stock at the bottom of one of the saw legs. Make sure that it is straight and flush with the bottom edge of the saw leg. Clamp it with a pair of vise grips and weld it in place. Weld on the outside edge only because the inside edge needs to remain smooth to allow for free travel of the blade tension bolt. To set the space for the tension bolt use a piece of 1/4" key stock as a blank. Place the blank on the saw leg against the piece that we just welded in place. Place one of the 3/4" long pieces of key stock against the blank, clamp it with a pair of vise grips, and weld it in place. Make sure that the blank still slides freely. Place a piece of 3/4" x 3/4"- 1/8" strap on top of the key stock and weld it in place. Repeat the same process for the other frame leg. Replace the blanks with tension bolts. Screw 1/4-20 wing nuts to the end of each tension bolt. The saw frame is now ready for a blade. See detail 50 on page 53.

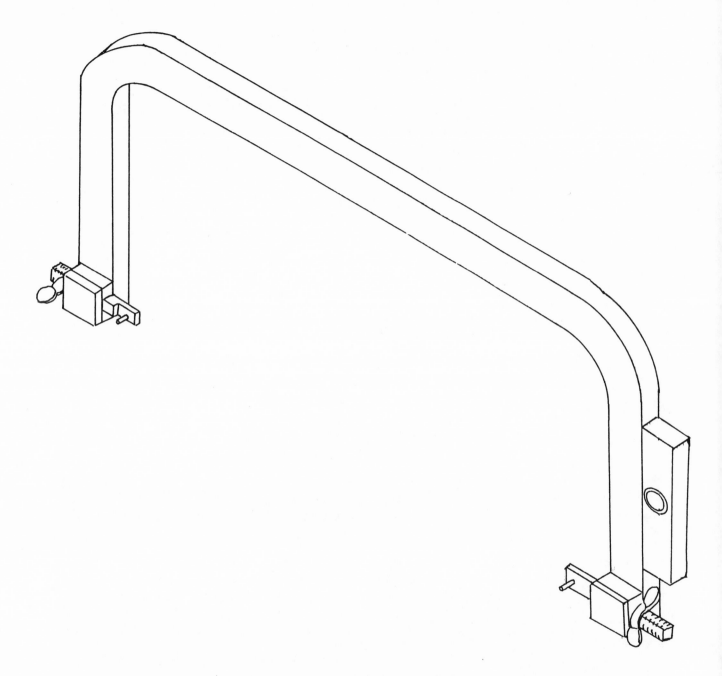

DETAIL- 50

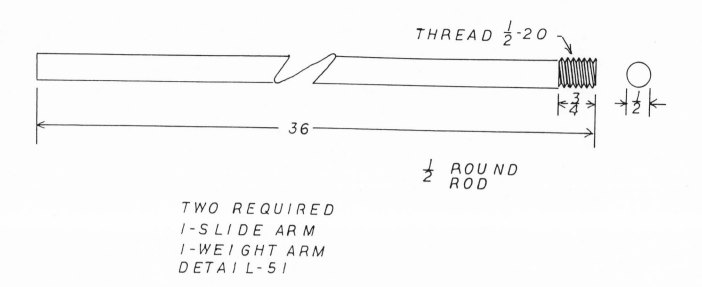

THREAD $\frac{1}{2}$-20

36

$\frac{3}{4}$

$\frac{1}{2}$

$\frac{1}{2}$ ROUND ROD

TWO REQUIRED
1-SLIDE ARM
1-WEIGHT ARM
DETAIL-51

SAW SLIDE ASSEMBLY

The saw slide and weight arms are simply two 36" sections of 1/2" round rod suitable for use with bronze bushings. One end of each rod is threaded 1/2-20. This enables us to thread each rod into the support pillar. See detail 51 on page 54.

The slide arm and weight arm stabilizer post is next. Cut a piece of 2" x 3/8" flat bar 8 1/2" long. Detail 52 on page 55 shows where to drill the holes that are required. The slide and weight arm fit in the top two holes that are drilled 1/2". Two holes are drilled and tapped 1/4-20 in the side of each of these 1/2" holes for set screws. By tightening these set screws against the slide and weight arm we are able to secure the stabilizer post. The 7/8" hole located in the stabilizer post is for the stabilizer casing which houses the bushing that the saw frame stabilizer rod slides through.

Cut two pieces of 1/2" black pipe 3 3/4" long. This will be the slide arm bushing assembly. See detail 53 on page 56. Press a 1/2" I.D. 5/8" O.D. bushing into each end of the black pipe. The black pipe that I used accepted a 1/2" bushing with a 5/8" outside diameter without having to drill it out. The bushing should fit snug, without distorting it, as you press it in. If it doesn't it's a simple matter to run a 5/8" drill through each end of the black pipe.

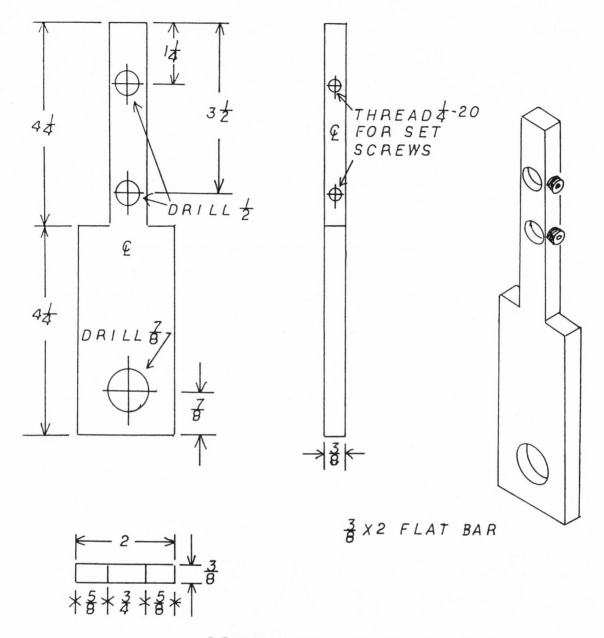

$\frac{3}{8}$ X2 FLAT BAR

STABILIZER POST
DETAIL-52

Cut two pieces of 1" x 1/8" strap 10" long. This is a little longer than needed, but we'll trim off the excess when we are done making the part. Each piece of strap will be wrapped around the 1/2" black pipe that was cut 3 3/4" long. These are referred to as hanger brackets and enable us to attach the slide bushing assembly to the saw frame. We'll need to make two of these brackets. To form the strap iron to fit the black pipe is simple. First look at detail 55 on page 57 to see what the finished bracket looks like. To bend it to shape place a scrap piece of 1/2" black pipe in a vise. Take one of the 10" pieces of strap and measure 5" from each end to find center. Clamp a pair of vise grips on each end of the strap for leverage. Line up the center line of the strap with the center of the black pipe and bend the strap around the pipe until it forms a horse shoe shape. Remove the vise grips. Remove the piece of pipe from the vise. With the strap still wrapped around the pipe place the horse shoe legs in the vise. Tighten the vise until the bracket is formed. Trim the legs to 1" in length.

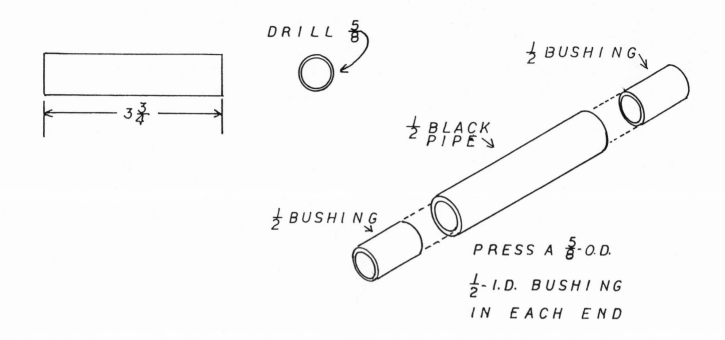

DRILL $\frac{5}{8}$

$\frac{1}{2}$ BUSHING

$\frac{1}{2}$ BLACK PIPE

$\frac{1}{2}$ BUSHING

$3\frac{3}{4}$

PRESS A $\frac{5}{8}$-O.D.

$\frac{1}{2}$-I.D. BUSHING

IN EACH END

SLIDE ARM BUSHING ASSEMBLY
DETAIL-53

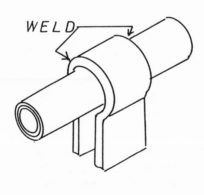

WELD

DETAIL-54

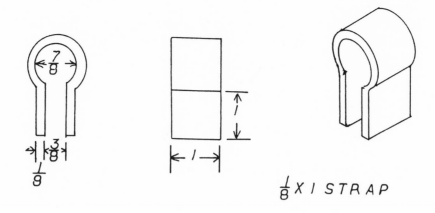

$\frac{1}{8} X I STRAP$

SLIDE ARM BUSHING HANGER BRACKET
DETAIL-55

Take the two brackets that we just made and slide the two pieces of 1/2" black pipe 3 3/4" long into them. Center the bracket and weld. Be careful not to over heat the pipe and damage the bushings. Also protect the bushings from weld splatter. A 1/2" long weld along the top of each side of the bracket is sufficient. See detail 54 on page 56 for a view of the slide bushing and hanger bracket assembly complete.

Refer to detail 56 on page 58 as we attach the slide arm bushing assembly hanger bracket to the saw frame. Place the two slide arm bushing assemblies on the slide arm. They should slide back and forth easily. If they don't you can free the action by sliding them back and forth several times using liquid graphite as a lubricant. Attach the saw frame to the hanger brackets. Line the bottom edge of the hanger brackets with the bottom edge of the top section of the saw frame. Double check to see that the saw frame is parallel to the slide arm. Position each bracket 1" from the inside of each saw frame leg. Clamp both brackets to the saw frame with vise grips and weld them in place. Be sure to protect the slide arm from weld splatter. Detail 57 on page 59 shows the saw frame complete with the slide bushing assembly.

Screw the slide arm and weight arm into the holes that are provided for them in the support pillar. See detail 58, on page 60.

Clamp a piece of material in the hacksaw vise and allow it to extend over the edge 4" or 5". This will give the saw frame something to rest on as we complete the project.

Put a saw blade in the saw frame. Make sure that the teeth of the saw blade face towards the rear or cut direction. Refer to detail 1 on page 4 for clarification of the cut direction. Slide the frame onto the slide arm. Make sure that the slide bushing assembly still slides freely. If not, work it back and forth a few times to free it up.

Place the stabilizer post in position at the end of the slide and weight arm. Tighten the set screws. Detail 58 on page 60 shows the slide arm, weight arm, saw frame and stabilizer post installed on the saw.

PROTECT SLIDE ARM
FROM WELD SPLATTER

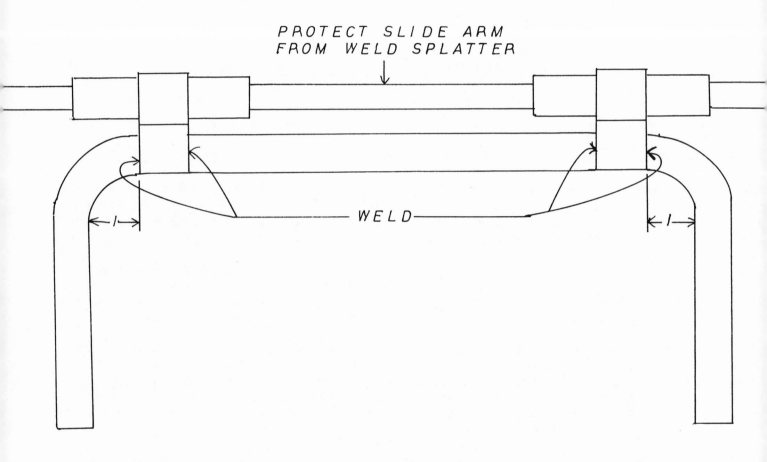

WELD

WELD SLIDE BUSHING
ASSEMBLY TO SAW FRAME
DETAIL-56

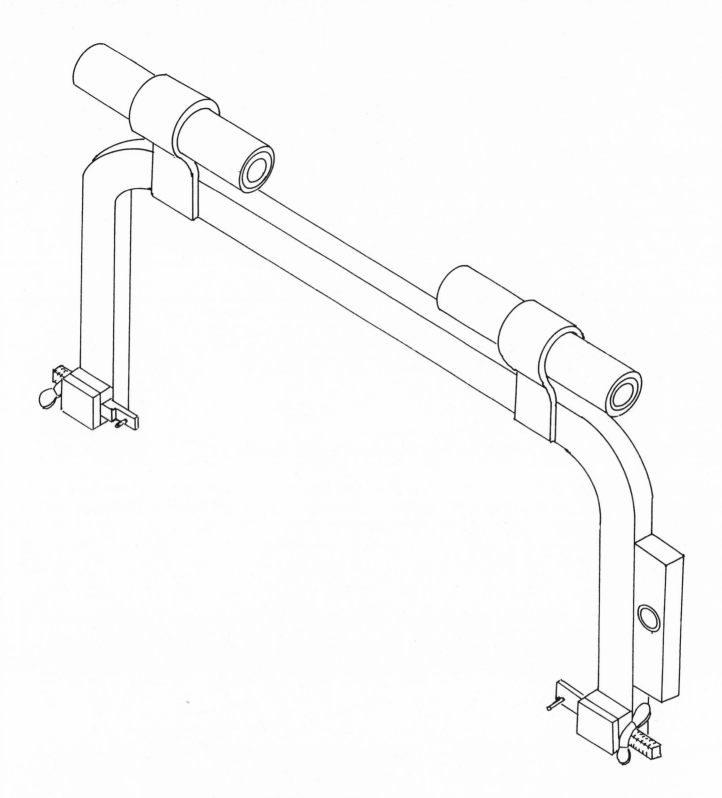

DETAIL-57

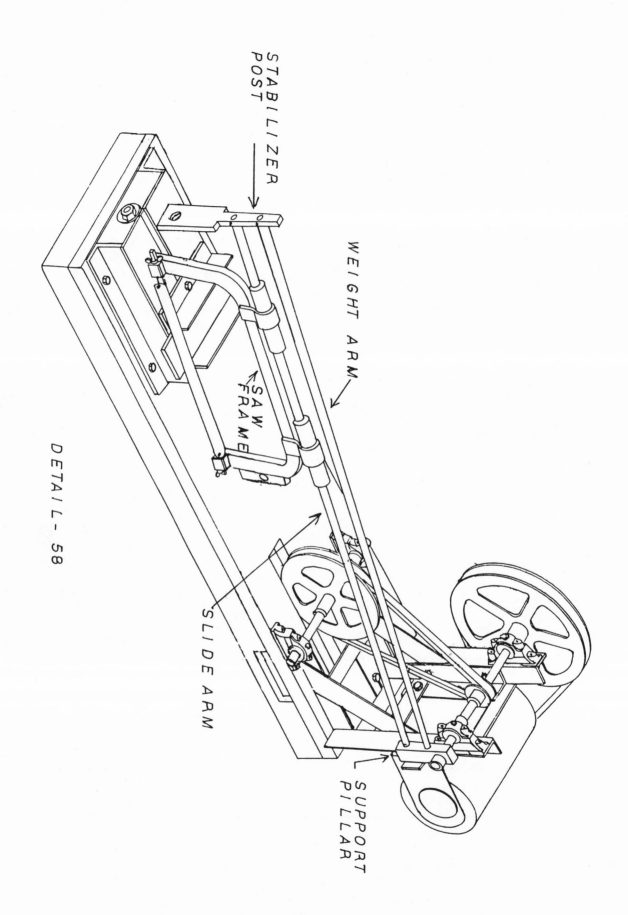

STABILIZER POST

WEIGHT ARM

SAW FRAME

DETAIL - 58

SLIDE ARM

SUPPORT PILLAR

60

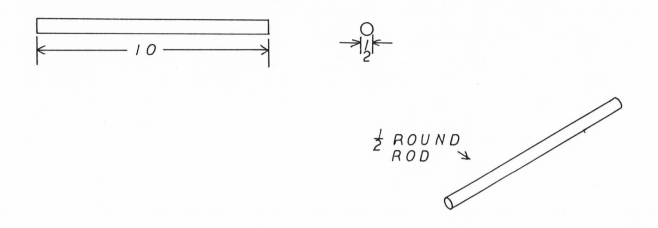

STABILIZER ROD
DETAIL 59

It is necessary to stabilize the bottom of the saw frame. To do that we will be welding a 10" piece of 1/2" round rod, suitable for use with bronze bushings, to the front of the saw frame. This will be referred to as the stabilizer rod. Detail 59 on page 61 shows a drawing of the stabilizer rod. Go ahead and cut the stabilizer rod at this time, but do not weld it to the saw frame yet.

The stabilizer rod will travel through a bushing that has been pressed into one end of a piece of 1/2" black pipe 10" long. One end of this piece of black pipe is threaded with standard 1/2" pipe threads so that an end cap can be screwed onto it. The piece of black pipe will be referred to as the stabilizer bushing housing. It is inserted in the 7/8" hole that is located in the bottom of the stabilizer post. Detail 60 on page 62 shows a drawing of the stabilizer bushing housing. Go ahead and cut the 10" piece of black pipe and press a 1/2" I.D. 5/8" O.D. bushing in one end of it. Mount the stabilizer bushing housing in the stabilizer post, as shown in detail 61 on page 62, but do not weld it in place at this time.

The saw frame stabilizer rod must be welded to the saw frame straight and in such a way as to slide in and out of the bushing housing freely. Insert one end of the stabilizer rod into the bushing housing and let the other end of it touch the saw frame. Measure the distance between the stabilizer rod and the slide arm at each end. Adjust the stabilizer rod up, or down to make the measurements on both ends equal. Refer to detail 62 on page 63 for clarification. When the measurements are equal tack weld the stabilizer rod to the saw frame. Be sure to only tack weld it in place at this time because it may have to be broken loose and reset if there is a binding problem.

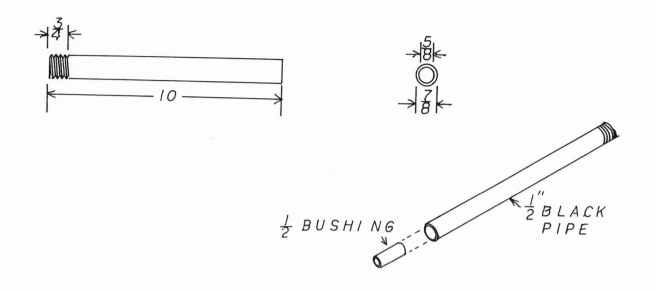

SAW FRAME STABILIZER
BUSHING CASING
DETAIL 60

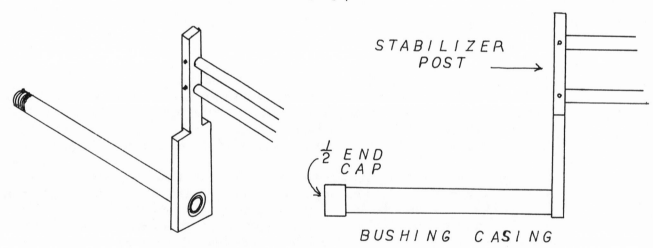

STABILIZER POST

BUSHING CASING

INSERT BUSHING CASING
INTO STABILIZER POST

DETAIL 61

As you slide the saw frame back and forth the stabilizer rod should travel freely in and out of the housing. Since we haven't welded the housing in place yet we can adjust it slightly one way, or the other until the stabilizer rod travels smoothly. If you still have a problem you may have to go back and remeasure the stabilizer rod to make sure it is straight. When things are sliding smoothly tack weld the housing to the stabilizer post. Be careful not to over heat it and cause the bushing to swell. A tack weld at the top, bottom and each side is sufficient.

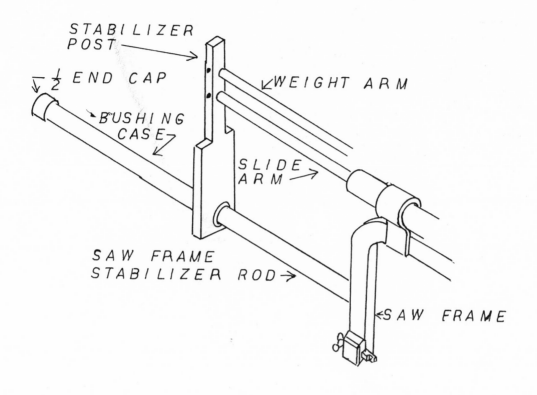

STABILIZER POST

END CAP

$\frac{1}{2}$

BUSHING CASE

WEIGHT ARM

SLIDE ARM

SAW FRAME STABILIZER ROD

SAW FRAME

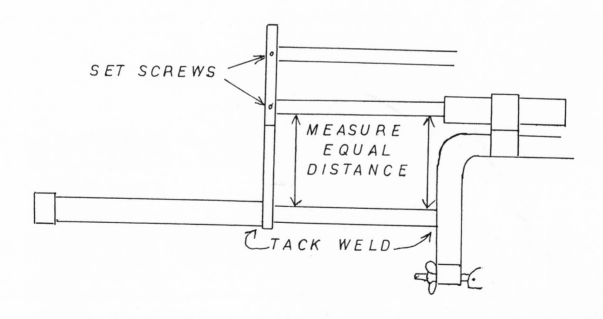

SET SCREWS

MEASURE EQUAL DISTANCE

TACK WELD

DETAIL-62

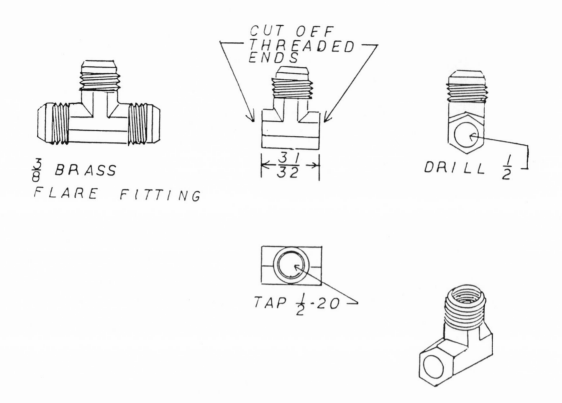

CUT OFF
THREADED
ENDS

$\frac{3}{8}$ BRASS
FLARE FITTING

$\frac{31}{32}$

DRILL $\frac{1}{2}$

TAP $\frac{1}{2}$-20

CONNECTING ROD BEARING
DETAIL-63

BUILDING THE CONNECTING ROD ASSEMBLY

Begin with the connecting rod bearing. It is made from a 3/8" brass union tee flare fitting. We will have to modify it to fit our needs. Refer to detail 63 on page 64 as I explain how this is done. The threaded parts on each side of the "T" section are cut off. Be careful not to cut to much off here because the width of the "T" section needs to be 31/32". If it is less than that there will be too much play in the bearing. If you do end up with to much play in the bearing a washer can be used to take up the slack. Detail 69 on page 68 shows a washer being used to reduce the amount of play in the bearing. Enlarge the hole through the "T" section to 1/2". Step drill this hole and be sure that it is drilled perfectly straight and no larger than 1/2". This is the bearing section. The post section of the "T" is drilled and tapped 1/2 - 20. The connecting rod is screwed into this hole. The connecting rod bearing is another one of those critical parts. How careful you are with this part determines how well the saw functions.

The connecting rod bearing is secured to the crank arm by a 1/2" x 1" shoulder bolt which is referred to as the stationary part of the connecting rod bearing. Detail 64 on page 65, shows a drawing of the shoulder bolt.

64

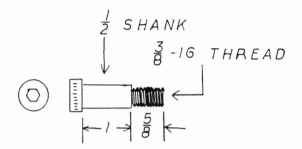

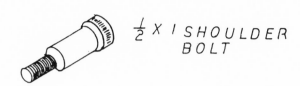

½ SHANK

⅜ -16 THREAD

½ X 1 SHOULDER BOLT

CRANK PIN
DETAIL 64

The clevis is represented in detail 65 on page 66. It can be purchased at your local hardware or farm supply store at a reasonable price.

The clevis is attached to the saw frame with a 1 5/8" x 1/2" clevis pin. The clevis pin is secured with a 1/2" washer and a 3/32" x 1 5/8" hitch pin. These parts are shown in detail 66 on page 66.

The connecting rod is a piece of 1/2" round rod 9 1/2" long threaded 1/2-20 on each end. The end threaded 1/2" back threads into the connecting rod bearing. The end that is threaded 1" back threads into the clevis. See detail 67 on page 66.

Detail 68 on page 67 shows a blow up view of the connecting rod assembly. Detail 69 on page 68 shows the saw complete.

FINISHING TOUCHES

I am sure you're anxious to get the saw up and running. Mount a switch box to the side of the base and install a single pole switch to operate the saw. Drill holes in the back of the base near the motor and run the wires under the base to the switch box. All wires should be ran in conduit. Make sure that the switch box and all wiring are secured and as far away as possible from any moving parts. Check all local codes, and insurance regulations to ensure that wiring meets any and all regulations.

Before you turn the power on, double check all of your work. Rotate the outboard pulley by hand several times to make sure that all moving parts move freely and that the saw does not bind. Be sure that all set screws are tight. Lubricate all of the moving parts slightly, except for the slide arm and saw frame stabilizer rod before you begin. I found that too much oil on the slide arm and the saw frame stabilizer rod would cause the saw to bind. These two areas of the saw run best with little or no oil. So when you oil these parts use the oil sparingly.

If you are sure that everything is ready go ahead and power up the saw, but be ready to turn it off immediately if there is a problem. Let the saw run for a few minutes to break in all of the parts. When you are satisfied that every thing is working properly turn the saw off. Clamp a piece of material in the vise and turn the saw back on. Lower the blade slowly to the work and let the saw start cutting.

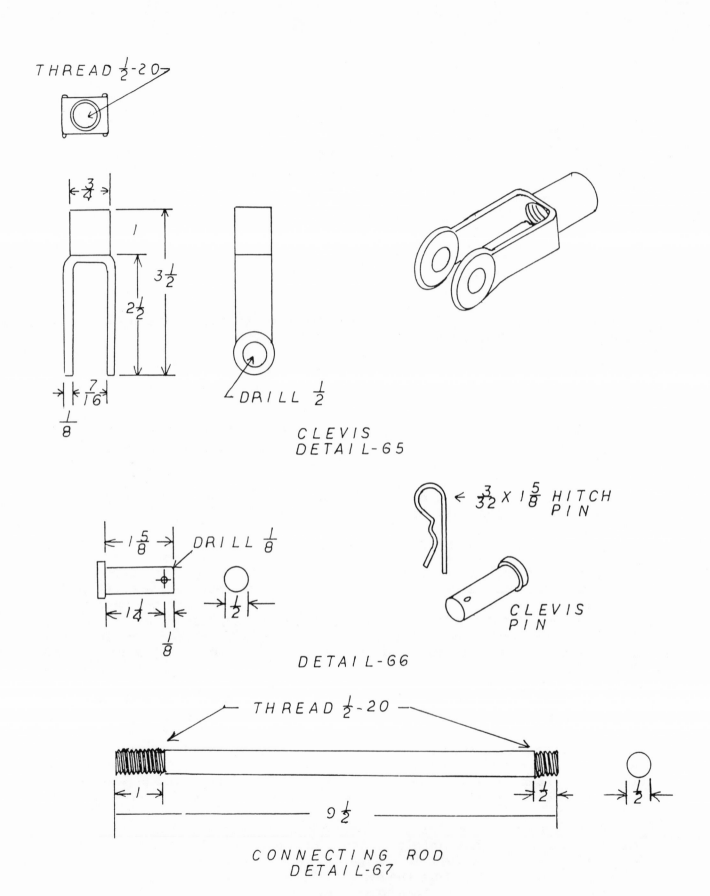

THREAD $\frac{1}{2}$-20

$\frac{3}{4}$

1

$3\frac{1}{2}$

$2\frac{1}{2}$

$\frac{7}{16}$

$\frac{1}{8}$

DRILL $\frac{1}{2}$

CLEVIS
DETAIL-65

$1\frac{5}{8}$ DRILL $\frac{1}{8}$

$1\frac{1}{4}$

$\frac{1}{8}$

$\frac{1}{2}$

$\frac{3}{32} \times 1\frac{5}{8}$ HITCH PIN

CLEVIS PIN

DETAIL-66

THREAD $\frac{1}{2}$-20

1

$9\frac{1}{2}$

$\frac{1}{2}$

$\frac{1}{2}$

CONNECTING ROD
DETAIL-67

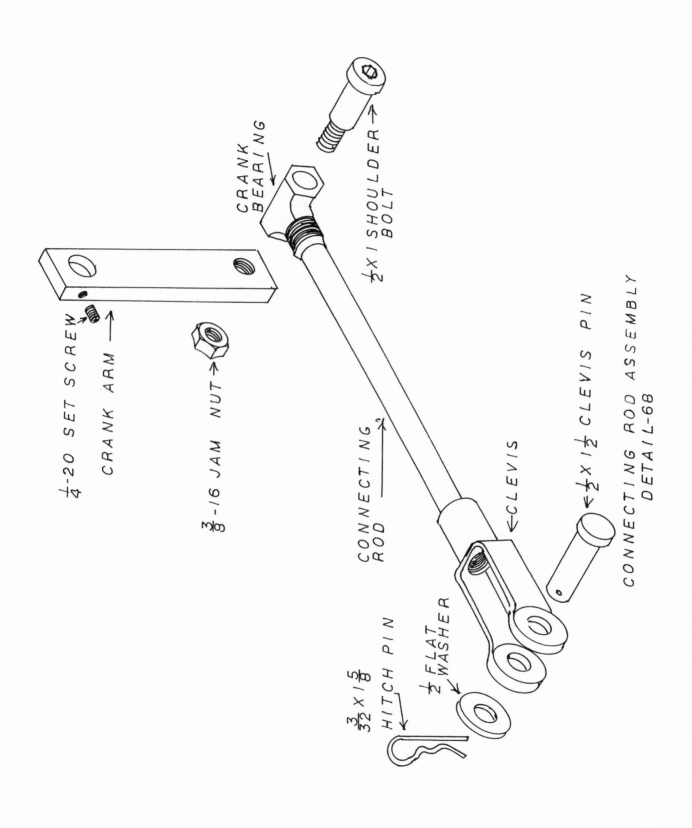

CRANK BEARING

$\frac{1}{4} \times 1$ SHOULDER BOLT

$\frac{1}{4}$-20 SET SCREW

CRANK ARM →

$\frac{3}{8}$-16 JAM NUT →

CONNECTING ROD →

← CLEVIS

$\frac{1}{2} \times 1\frac{1}{2}$ CLEVIS PIN

CONNECTING ROD ASSEMBLY
DETAIL-68

$\frac{3}{32} \times 1\frac{5}{8}$
HITCH PIN

$\frac{1}{2}$ FLAT
WASHER

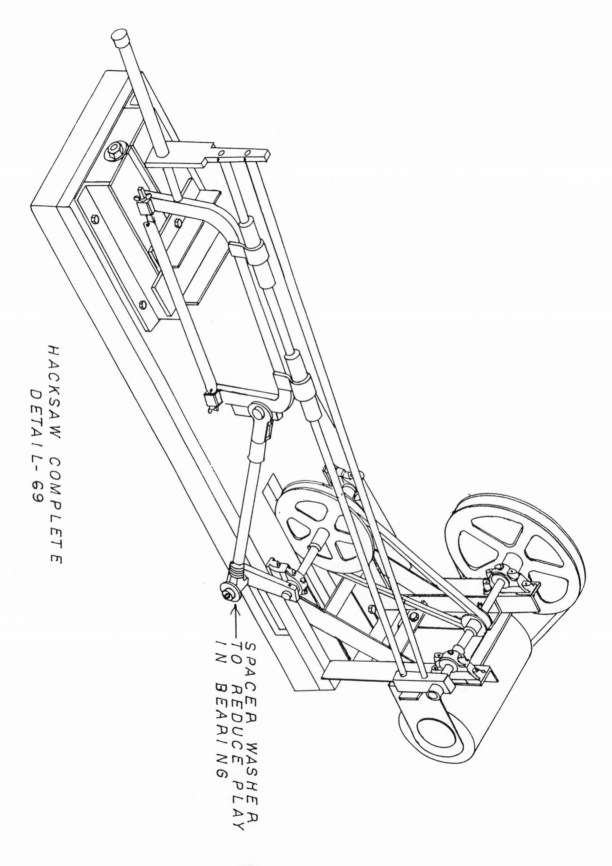

HACKSAW COMPLETE
DETAIL-69

SPACER WASHER
TO REDUCE PLAY
IN BEARING

Very little coolant, or lubricant is required on the saw blade as it cuts. I tried a couple of different lubricants on the saw blade as it was cutting. Soap suds was used by old timers, but I found when I used it, it caused things to rust. A light weight machine oil added to the blade when it seemed to be binding, and getting hot worked best of all. Be careful though if the oil is to heavy it seems to cause the metal chips to clot up and causes more problems than it solves.

Chances are, your saw will run fine and cut straight. But if it doesn't, here are a few areas to check:

1. Check to see if the saw frame is square with the work. If it is not it can be adjusted by loosening the set screws on the stabilizer post and twisting the stabilizer post either left or right. When you do this it also moves the saw frame. When the saw frame is straight re-tighten the set screws.

2. Check to see if the saw blade sits in the frame straight. This can be corrected by bending the blade pins up or down.

3. Make sure that the holes in the slide arm support pillar, crank arm and crank arm bearing have been drilled straight.

4. Check to see if the countershaft stand is mounted on the base straight. Also, check the crankshaft, countershaft and vise to be sure they are mounted straight.

5. Your blade may be coming down to hard on the work and twisting when you first start the cut. The saw frame needs to be let down easy when you first start the cut. When the cut gets started you can let go of the frame and the saw will do it's work.

Well congratulations you have just finished building your very own power hacksaw and a first class vise as well. I'm sure your arms are saying thanks too, because with luck they will never have to use a hand hacksaw again. I hope you enjoyed the project as much as I have. I'm sure it will give you years of satisfaction and service.